Ignition

A Professional Woman's
Guide to Energized,
Burnout-Proof Living

Chris Vasiliadis

MOMENT ONE PUBLISHING

Published by Moment One Publishing: www.momentonepublishing.com

First edition: March 2019

Editor: Kate Victory Hannisian, Blue Pencil Consulting
Book and Cover Design: Lisa McKenna, Arrow North
Photo credits:
    Author photo: Mira Whiting Photography
    Cover photo: Lightboxx, stock.adobe.com

ISBN: 978-0-578-43533-6

Contents

Inspired by and in memory of my father, Jim,
who asked me in a strong voice, with his beautiful blue eyes
shining and his smile beaming, two weeks before he died:
"So, Christine, are you setting the world on fire yet?"

Introduction

Burning the candle at both ends? Health on the back burner? Feeling like the status quo of how you're living and running your life is unsustainable for your health and well-being? Do you know you want to make changes, but you don't know where to begin? *Ignition* will guide you to your answers. Before we start you on your path to creating a plan for energized living, let me first tell you a story about the medical diagnosis that led me to change my profession, and to explain why I care so much about helping others prevent burnout in their own lives.

"Hmm ... that's odd ... my legs have gone numb from my knees down. I don't remember hurting my back." These were the thoughts running through my head that October 2005 day as I worked an event at Boston's Saks Fifth Avenue as a freelance makeup artist for Bobbi Brown. At that time, my other work included makeup services for weddings and professionals, plus marketing consulting for solo practitioners and small business owners (ah, the joys of being an entrepreneur!). This numbness triggered a series of medical events over the next couple months, including being prescribed Prednisone to calm the inflammation in my body, having an MRI of my brain and spine, and getting a second opinion and more tests.

I endured a second attack the night before Thanksgiving that included a night of vertigo and vomiting. I woke up on Thanksgiving morning with double vision: a classic multiple sclerosis (MS) symptom. (MS is a chronic disease of the central nervous system, for which there is no cure. Besides numbness, tingling and double vision, other symptoms include fatigue and issues with mobility, pain, cognition, swallowing and incontinence.) In order to see straight, I had to wear an eye patch for five to six weeks until the double vision abated. Looking back, those weeks were the scariest part of my diagnosis, as I wasn't sure I'd be able to see straight again.

I was ultimately diagnosed with MS on December 2, on the second day of getting an infusion of Solu-Medrol (a steroid that treats inflammation). Because I wanted to keep my diagnosis a secret from anyone but close family and friends, while I wore the eye patch I used the excuse that I had an eye infection that needed to be covered up.

I had a brief moment where I felt this diagnosis wasn't supposed to happen to me. After all, I was forty years old and pretty healthy (I thought), and my parents and three of my grandparents were still living. There were no other MS cases in my family, and at the time, there was no cancer in my family (although that would change within the next year).

I can remember reading a statistic when I was diagnosed that only 15% of people with MS end up in a wheelchair. I first cited that statistic when I shared my diagnosis with my parents, who immediately thought I would someday be like celebrity Annette Funicello of movie and Disney "Mouseketeers" fame. She had severe, debilitating effects from MS, including impaired speech and swallowing issues, and needed to use a wheelchair. I was emboldened by those statistics at that time, and wanted to do everything I could to end up in the 85% bracket. In hindsight, I see that I accepted my diagnosis pretty much on the spot, and made a January appointment to see my primary care physician (PCP). I can remember with distinct clarity starting that meeting with this statement: "Okay, I have this MS diagnosis, and it's my intention to lead a fully active, healthy life. What should I be doing?"

This was my ignition: the start of making my wellness a priority in my own life, and the eventual inspiration for writing this book to help you do the same, whether the spur for you is a chronic illness, a life transition, or a persistent inner voice that has been urging you to move out of an energetic rut, break your inertia, steer yourself away from burnout, and get your booster rockets going again.

These days, in my career, I specialize in helping professional women move from:

- exhausted to engaged,
- frazzled to fueled, and
- perpetually on autopilot to being present.

I don't come to you with a silver bullet solution. As I've witnessed in over ten years of health coaching countless clients, there is no one "right" or single way to achieve the energy and vitality you desire. That's actually part of what makes my job so much fun: helping my clients figure out the right combination of techniques that works for them.

However, I have noticed patterns and ways to approach such change that increase the likelihood of success.

That's what this book is about.

My Indirect Path from MS to Health Coaching

My own journey began with 2006 evolving into what I dubbed the "Year of the Lab Rat." I began daily injections of one of the MS disease-modifying drugs. My PCP lined me up with all kinds of allergy tests, which led to additional blood work, candida treatment and food elimination plans. I dabbled in Qigong, an ancient Chinese exercise and healing technique that involves meditation, controlled breathing and movement exercises. Qigong, pronounced *CHEE-GONG*, literally means "life energy work" – a way of working with one's life energy. This program was offered by one of the physicians at my doctor's office, to further help me manage and give me more energy. Severe fatigue is often a symptom of MS; that year, I needed a nap pretty much every day to function. By the end of all the testing in October 2006 (one year after my initial MS symptoms appeared), I was diagnosed non-celiac gluten-sensitive (and therefore stopped eating gluten). I also started taking several supplements for areas in which my blood labs and other testing showed I was deficient, and to tame my immune system and fight inflammation.

I wasn't able to stand for long periods of time that first year, so I stopped doing freelance makeup artistry, and over the next year, weaned off doing any makeup work with private clients. I would have another MS relapse for a week or two in January 2007 where it felt like my hands and feet were tingling to the extent they felt on fire 24/7. I also experienced this sensation, called banding, in my torso, which felt like I was wearing an extremely tight girdle.

Fast-forward to late 2007. I had learned that deliberately managing my energy in a way that supported my health was essential to avoid burning myself out and to minimize the chances of further MS relapses. I was now performing marketing consulting as my sole work, and had gone public about my MS that summer. I didn't make some big announcement on social media: I opted to gradually extend the circle of people I informed about my health status. It took me some time to be comfortable with sharing this news and handling people's reactions. They ranged from curiosity to "Oh, my aunt died from that," to "So, you're one of Jerry's Kids?" (This last one is a reference to a charity for muscular dystrophy, *not* multiple sclerosis. Sigh.)

One day, I was getting ready to meet one of my favorite clients, a career coach, and I wasn't looking forward to it. It's always been important to me to enjoy the work I do, and to feel like I'm providing value. After a bit of soul-searching, I thought to myself, "Okay, you do work that helps people with their own business figure out ways to get more clients. That helps them put food on the table, so there's value there. But at the end of the day, if they're not healthy, this means bubkes."

That was my lightbulb moment. I now knew I wanted to work in an area where I could help others attain their desired level of health and wellness.

After I completed that project with the career coach, I looked at her, smiled, and said, "Now *I* need to hire *you*." I knew I didn't want another degree (my bachelor's degree is in computer science and my master's degree is in education), and I wasn't interested in becoming a doctor, nurse or social worker. Working with this coach and conducting additional networking led to me becoming trained and certified as a Health and Wellness Coach through Wellcoaches, while simultaneously getting certified as a Personal Trainer through the American College of Sports Medicine. I launched my new company, Priority Wellness, in the fall of 2008.

I began by focusing on helping individuals with stress management. Then and now, my clients engage with me through one-on-one coaching (primarily via phone), group coaching, or seminars and workshops. I also work directly with companies as a dedicated health coach for their employees, and with healthcare providers as a health coach for their patients. Today, having since added National Board Certified Health & Wellness Coach to my credentials, my specialty has evolved into helping professional women (generally in their forties and older) who are at, approaching, or concerned about burnout, to elevate their energy and vitality. It makes me really sad to see women bouncing from thing to thing to thing on autopilot, going through the motions, riding the edge of burnout or already in it, thinking that's the way their life has to be, or trying to create self-worth from all their to-dos. Your value already exists, my reader friend: you were *born* worthy!

My MS diagnosis was my wake-up call to make significant lifestyle changes, to protect me from burning myself out, and to minimize future attacks and declines in my health. I'm grateful to have been relapse-free since January 2007, am in the best shape I've ever been, and possess routine strong energy. I attribute that to a combination of luck, genes, and many intentional choices about how I consistently live, design and fuel my life.

I want to help as many people as possible prioritize their well-being, and use that as their secret weapon to being engaged in and successfully leading their work and non-work lives. I see optimal health – through energized, burnout-proof living – as a tool, enabling you to contribute in ways important to you, instead of wearing yourself out. However, I know I can't privately coach every single person who would benefit from this guidance. This fact, along with a love for books and reading, is what led me to write *Ignition*. I want to get this information into the hands of professional women like you who are unhappy with their current level of energy and vitality, feel like they're running themselves into the ground, and who want something different.

With this book, I want to give you a real-life approach to creating an energized lifestyle in accessible ways. You need only show up as you are, and be open and willing to make changes to start burnout-proof living. You'll play with some aspects of this approach temporarily, while you'll decide to put others in place longer term. Plan to take your strengths along for the ride, and be prepared to unpack and adjust some stories along the way. You are about to step into new ways of *doing* in your life and new ways of *being* to gain the energy and vitality you crave. Collectively, these principles from my own life experience, wise influencers in related areas, and the sage lessons learned from my clients and other women furnish the tips and practical examples of the "how" and "what" of this process.

The examples throughout this book showcase professional women in their forties and above, as this is my niche in my health coaching practice. This is the population I know best. If you're not part of that demographic, you are still welcome to come along for the ride: there will likely be multiple parts of *Ignition* that will help you create your own ways of energized, burnout-proof living.

Instead of prioritizing work-life balance, I advocate starting with a foundation of *inner* balance. If you're trying to create work-life balance from a frenzied way of being, that typically will result in clouded or unbalanced results. Alternatively, when you are grounded from within, you enhance the clarity of your lens. From that frame of reference, it's easier to see what's right for and best serves you in the moment. That's the crux of what *Ignition* addresses: what works for you at this phase in your life.

My wish for you is to experience the optimal level of energy and vitality that you're capable of attaining. If you feel your inner light has dimmed or shut down, you can re-ignite that flame. Your prize? Living above the chaos in the most alive way possible, imprinting your unique mark on the world. Remembering, deeply, who you are and living from that place. The reward for those you touch? They will benefit from witnessing who and how you're being, and your contributions. In fact, your light may inspire them to carry their own torch and blaze their own trail. You can be part of a movement that creates a ripple effect of energized and burnout-proof living cultivated by our female colleagues, mothers, sisters, daughters, nieces, those we mentor and other women in our lives. When we shine, we and others thrive. Ignite your own vitality and join this fired-up movement. Glad to have you on board!

How to Use This Book

Go through this book at a pace that works for you. On most of the exercises, I have not provided time limits, preferring to keep you in the driver's seat. Some exercises might be easy for you to complete quickly, while others will require you to spend more time to go in more depth. You have permission to follow your own energy, and trust that you'll know what you need to do and how far you need to go, to address your self-care. You might especially notice any resistance that occurs when you first read an exercise. Instead of dismissing an exercise when this happens, consider the opportunity to learn a new way or point of view, a different way of doing or being, even if it's initially uncomfortable. Here's what we'll cover as we go through this book together.

Part One: Start Your Engines (Chapters 1-3)

Chapters 1-3 are the core foundation pieces. I recommend you start there, as these chapters guide you in designing your path through Chapters 4 through 9. Chapters 1 (The Starting Gate: From Autopilot to Aware) and 2 (Affirm Your Strengths and Supporting Energies) help you figure out where you are now and your starting point. In Chapter 3 (The Burnout-Proofing Dashboard and Your Wellness Vision), I'll introduce you to a tool and accompanying self-assessment to choose which chapters to read next, from Part Two.

Part Two: Cruise Pathways of Doing and Being (Chapters 4 -9)
While reading the chapters you select from 4 through 9, you are, in a sense, traveling your own unique path through the new patterns you'll experiment with and implement. These chapters are titled Foster Your Inner Balance, Dance with Loving Acceptance and Self-Compassion, Practice Presence-Driven Focus, Play in Energized Places, Maximize Your Energy Intelligence, and Cultivate Relationships and Social Connections. Through a combination of other women's stories and related exercises, tips, and questions to ask yourself, these chapters help you identify your own customized ways to ignite and shine. You may decide to perform your chosen Part Two chapters' exercises, tips and principles as you go, and/or use Chapter 10's action plan building blocks to create a list for later implementation.

Part Three: Blast Off and Shine (Chapters 10 – 12)
Chapter 10 (Ignite Burnout-Proof Patterns) provides the structure for a ninety-day action plan using your chosen elements for living in a burnout-proof way. Chapter 11 (Negotiate Hurdles Along the Way) identifies common challenges (and their work-arounds) in instilling new patterns, and Chapter 12 (Celebrate Your Success and Join an Ignited Movement) wraps up with some motivation to both begin now and be part of a community of women working on re-igniting their energy and resilient ways of living.

While there is space for you to write in the book as you try different exercises, you may find that having a notebook or journal available to write in instead will help you think through each chapter's content. Also consider that you may reuse and revisit *Ignition* in future phases of your life, and you may have different areas of focus or responses to the prompts at that time. In any case, progressing through *Ignition* will require writing in parts, so please decide now where you'd like to do that.

As you move through this book, if you haven't done this recently, start noticing your current behavior and internal responses in related aspects of your health and wellness. Set aside any judgment you might feel – simply notice. For example, notice how you feel when you sit down to a meal: are you even sitting at a dining table? Notice the thoughts in your head when you wake up in the morning. What are you thinking about the day ahead? What do your mind and body feel like at different parts of the day, or in different situations? Is there a time of day when you feel more or less "on"?

Let me assure you: wherever you're starting from is the right place. There is no ideal time to begin. I say that as a recovering Type A personality, with a past record of sometimes waiting for things to line up perfectly before I took action. All you need in order to begin is to want a different outcome than what you have at this moment, to be willing to play with new approaches, and new ways of thinking, acting and being. I'm ready to meet you where you are. Are you ready to ignite your energy and vitality?

I also encourage you to bring a friend along with you for the ride. I've seen multiple examples of women partnering with like-minded buddies to make changes aimed at improving their well-being and how partnership tends to increase the likelihood of success. What other professional women in your world might share your desire to live with more energy and vitality? You could work your way through this book with one person or a group of women, either in person (through your personal network or something like a Meetup group) or via email, Facebook, or other social media or online tool. For added camaraderie, I also invite you to join the Women Igniting Energized Burnout-Proof Living Facebook Group.[1]

Let's begin burnout-proof living so you can shine your light.

---

1 www.facebook.com/groups/IgnitionGroup

Part One:
Start Your Engines

CHAPTER ONE

The Starting Gate: From Autopilot to Aware

"Thoughts can keep you from your experience. Your life doesn't exist in your head. It exists in being alive."

~ PATRICIA HOWARD

large chunk of my health coaching work involves helping clients see where they're getting in their own way. Many women have a habit of being continuously "on" and not routinely stopping to catch their breath or come up for air. When we pause to identify the thoughts and behaviors that are working for and against us, and see that we're not alone in this way of being, we then have an opportunity to make different choices to elevate our health. If you've had a gnawing feeling of wanting to make changes, but haven't been able to get started or make headway, this chapter will grease the skids for you.

I find that sometimes it can be difficult to look within, especially when you feel like you're in the depths of running your life and barely keeping your head above water. If this is where you are, the lives and examples of others can provide a mirror that helps you to reflect on your own behavior. Below, and throughout the book through Chapter 9, are experiences from professional women I've either coached or interviewed for *Ignition*. Where requested, I've changed the names to protect their privacy, and in some cases, have created composite examples to further keep these women anonymous.

Do any of these women's stories sound familiar to you?

Diane has hit a wall. She is the mother of three young children, has had a recent promotion at work, and has a husband who works long hours. In her early forties and overweight, she longs for quality sleep and has joined Weight

Watchers because she wants to lose weight. She participates in Fitbit challenges once in a while. Long-term, she wants to focus on having health and stamina as she ages. She feels that making or taking time to focus on herself doesn't seem possible.

Sabrina is in her early fifties, is the mother of two college-age children and is a successful real estate professional. While her physical health is top-notch, as she considers the next phase of her life, she wants to intentionally focus more on other life aspects that are now worthy of her time and energy. Her initial challenge is to avoid saying yes to every request, whether from clients, charitable organizations, or friends and family.

Anita, a senior-level employee in her late fifties, describes her life as on the go, nonstop. While she wants to lose weight, her efforts are currently challenged by frequently eating on the go, and by her husband's present medical needs. She also has a special needs child. She finds it hard to stay motivated to take the steps she knows would benefit her own self-care efforts.

Elaine is a single academic professional in her mid-sixties. Having recently cut back her work hours to prepare for retirement, she is challenged with the absence of structure on her days off. She wants to continue to be useful, while aging healthily and well.

While the specifics may be different for you, similar themes abound in the personal stories of many professional women. You have multiple responsibilities on your plate, and you repeat the task cycle every day, at times feeling like you're juggling and expecting to drop one or more balls at any moment. More often than not, you feel that you're skimming the surface of life instead of deeply engaging in it. Part of you wants something different for yourself, yet you put your health and well-being on the back burner, or push yourself further away from a solution and a more optimal way of fostering your wellness.

Our reasons for clinging to the status quo will vary, but in my work with my clients I've observed these common barriers to getting out of the starting gate:

- You can't see an alternative,
- You don't pause to self-assess your situation,

- You don't know where to begin to change, and/or
- You feel uncomfortable asking for help, or don't know where to get help.

If you find yourself in one of these scenarios, I encourage you to read on, as *Ignition* addresses each of these points.

Besides excess weight and depleted energy, functioning on chronic autopilot carries additional risks to your personal well-being, including stress, high blood pressure, under-nourishment, burnout, and missing out on life-affirming moments.

BURNOUT SELF-ASSESSMENT: Psychiatrist Dr. Philippe Weston defines burnout as "a syndrome of depleted emotional, physical and cognitive energies, cynical attitudes and feelings of personal ineffectiveness and incompetence." To self-assess whether you're at or approaching burnout, consider the past two weeks. Have you been experiencing a few of these symptoms on a regular basis?

- ☐ feeling exhausted/depleted
- ☐ forgetting things
- ☐ being distracted
- ☐ running on autopilot or feeling addicted to being busy
- ☐ insomnia
- ☐ loss of appetite
- ☐ feeling anxious or depressed
- ☐ being prone to anger or irritation
- ☐ mentally distancing yourself/checking out

If you haven't had these symptoms, great! What I'll share with you in *Ignition* will continue to help you to proactively ward off burnout and live with steady, consistent energy.

If any of the above symptoms *have* been part of your experience for the past two weeks, you may be at or approaching burnout. The light of life within you feels dimmed. What additional impact do you think that's having on the values you want to emulate and the messages you want to broadcast as you're putting yourself out there?

If you've experienced any of these symptoms for a longer period, and you feel that rectifying the situation requires more than lifestyle changes, consider consulting with your doctor. They may help determine whether any underlying medical conditions could be causing your symptoms.

What else can keep us stuck in our present ways of functioning? The disempowering stories we tell ourselves about our current situation. Think of a story as a thought or declaration that you feel is true and live by. Diane's story, for example, is that "time to focus on me doesn't seem possible." Other stories may or may not be consciously expressed and can include low-energy language like the following:

- "I put everyone else's needs first and mine last."
- "This is the way my life has to be for now."
- "It's mentally challenging for me to find a way to exercise."
- "It's easy for me to make excuses not to take care of myself."
- "My routine is interrupted constantly."
- "I'm the only one who can _____." (*fill in the blank*)
- "I avoid setting health and well-being goals because I self-sabotage my success."
- "I should be able to do it all."

Do you feel inspired to make changes if these are the stories you tell yourself? Probably not. When we believe and align our actions with such bleak stories and feel like they're unchangeable, we may end up constantly repeating the cycle. Such stories sabotage us before we even get out of the starting gate of change. We can unconsciously assign meaning to these stories, cement them as "truth," and disempower ourselves in the process. Treating these types of stories as fact, without questioning their reality or truthfulness, translates into the outlook and energy we bring to our days. Remaining unaware of these limiting beliefs on the path of change is like walking with lead weights in our shoes and having blinders on: it slows our progress and prevents us from seeing alternative ways of being.

Believing these stories is the ego at work: that voice in the head that scolds and chastises us, and that feels heavy, dark, and constrictive. One of my favorite authors, Eckhart Tolle, in his book *A New Earth*, describes a major aspect of the human dysfunction as "ego." He defines ego as an "illusory sense of self" based on unconsciously identifying with one's memories and thoughts. In other words, attaching meaning to who we are based on our past and our habitual thinking.

Ego can cause hurdles or delays in making changes for your own well-being.

This concept comes up frequently in my health coaching work: clients postpone getting started because they feel like they should have been able to make changes already on their own. Piling on the "shoulds" and the associated guilt and shame creates heavy emotional and judgmental baggage, even a sense of embarrassment. We can be so overwhelmed by the possibility of failure, and more crippling, the *meaning* that we place on that potential outcome, that we are stuck in our tracks. One detrimental perception of a situation can start a downward spiral of endless negative narratives that pull us down. Further down the road, in the midst of making change, what we say about ourselves (and many women have a habit of saying less-than-flattering things) can also stifle our efforts to move forward. Words hold powerful energy: what is the tone of the voice and the nature of the words you use when you talk to yourself?

Byron Katie, author of *Loving What Is* and creator of The Work,[1] a process for questioning thoughts, offers a powerful perspective on this notion: "A thought is harmless unless we believe it. It's not our thoughts, but our attachment to our thoughts, that causes suffering. Attaching to a thought means believing that it's true, without inquiring. A belief is a thought that we've been attaching to, often for years." Once you're aware of such attachments and how they're stifling your energy and capabilities, you don't have to continue to live with that situation. Your stories are changeable.

How do *you* begin to be in charge instead of letting the ego – and these stories – drive your life and health? How do you create new, empowering stories that you believe in and that pull you toward ignited energy?

Let me start by saying this is more like a lifelong practice than something you can change overnight or with a snap of your fingers. The place to begin is *noticing*. Catch yourself when the voice in your head is judging you or someone else. Observe, and bringing curiosity to the thought. Maybe even chuckle about your mental commentary from time to time. Use your moments of watching and catching yourself as a trigger to simply be present. As Byron

1 www.thework.com

Katie says, ask yourself, "Who would you be without that thought?"

Instead of living and working within a story that we have concocted in our minds, releasing the ego and its associated limiting beliefs allows us to live and work with what *is*, in this moment, right in front of us. Think of the ego as the voice inside that identifies ourselves through characteristics like our possessions, qualities and accomplishments. When we are aware of and let go of the ego, it opens the door so we can view situations with fresh eyes: no story, identity or past habitual perspective to hold us back or restrict our perceived options.

As I frequently say to my clients, "Awareness is the first step."

EXERCISE ONE: IDENTIFY YOUR CURRENT STORY

You picked up this book because you want more energy and vitality in your life. Maybe you know the stories you're telling yourself about your current life. Maybe you haven't stopped to consider them yet. Well, now is the time. The world at large has been waiting for you to bring forth the gems within you, and your best energy is available for you to soar and lead an engaged, resilient life of vitality. Picture me holding the space for you as you read the tips and perform the various activities in this book, supporting you to make this happen. I am projecting a full heart and acceptance for you as I write *Ignition*, and my intention is for that energy to be conveyed to you with each word you read. Visualize a virtual hug and/or loving energy from me surrounding you any time you need it as you go through *Ignition*.

Give yourself some physical and mental space for reflection, and think about the story you tell yourself about your current life situation. Ask yourself one or more of the following questions to help spark your thinking. If you have trouble with this process, ask a trusted friend for their honest perspective.

- How do you talk about yourself or how do you describe your current life situation to others?
- What is a common refrain you utter either out loud or in your head?
- What feels like a reason for the way things are for you? (It could even feel like an excuse for not changing.)
- What do your habitual actions say about your feelings towards your life, your attention to your health and wellness, and how you're currently showing up in the world?

The story that I've been telling myself and accepting is:

Now that you can see that story written down, how does it make you feel? Does it give you hope and optimism, or is it self-defeating? Does the story feel open, light and expansive, or does it close off and constrict possibilities?

If your current story instills negativity, you have the ability to change it. You can refocus, shift direction, and elevate your life. As Caroline Myss (five-time *New York Times* best-selling author and internationally renowned speaker in the fields of human consciousness, spirituality and mysticism, health, energy medicine, and the science of medical intuition) has stated, "Use the power of discernment. Decide what perception you will not allow into your orbit. Discernment is a navigator."

You may not be used to being your own cheerleader, taking a stand for yourself and your health, using your voice, showing the true authentic you. I understand that this may be new territory for you, and the thoughts of what's ahead may cause discomfort, uncertainty, and even touches of anxiety and fear for you. Note those thoughts, feelings and emotions, but realize that there's no need to become consumed by them. Together, we're helping you to train yourself in your new way of operating. Be prepared to shed some prior approaches that held you back and exchange them for fresh options that propel you forward. I'm excited for you, and I encourage you to tap into that part of you that's excited too!

EXERCISE TWO: CREATE AN ENERGIZING STORY

To begin on the path toward igniting your energy and vitality, clean the slate by tossing the stifling stories and giving yourself a fresh start with more invigorating narratives. How do you want to relate to yourself or to the world? Create a story that inspires you and pulls you forward. Since we're always making up stories anyway, why not create one with positive energy behind it? You're aiming for a story that includes authentic declarations with uplifting power, to refocus your energy and reframe your outlook. What is your new burnout-proof life view and what are your high-quality predictions for the type of person you want to be? Here are some examples:

- "I am consistently nourishing myself."
- "When I take care of myself first, I'm better able to help others."
- "I am prioritizing the actions that fuel my energy and vitality."
- "Figuring out what works best for my well-being is a long-term practice. I enjoy experimenting with what works for me now."
- "I am great at seeing the resources available to me that help me stay energized."

The following principles can help you access the story that works best for you now:

- Realize the story you create doesn't have to be the be-all-end-all. Let go of perfection here.
- The story is a statement or two that leans in a positive direction, and gives you a motivational spark.
- Give yourself some quiet time to be still and listen. This might mean a quiet room in your home, or someplace outside in nature. This will help you "hear" the small voice inside. It's likely the voice that's been waiting for you to stop, begging you to pay attention, and urging you to change gears. This is the voice of your true self, the authentic you. The voice that is innate, always there and wants the best for you.

If you're not used to putting yourself first or allowing time and space for yourself, this exercise can feel a bit uncomfortable. The pushback I sometimes get from my clients is that this type of activity feels selfish. I counter by asking, what if your best friend were in this same situation, and about to embark on a more energized and vital life? Would you discourage your friend? If your best friend was beside you right now, what would she or he tell you about taking this step? I encourage you to start considering your self-care as sacred. Be your own best friend through this process. Play with that idea and the notion of sacred self-care while you're reading this book and doing the exercises. Fundamental change starts now.

YOUR NEW ENERGIZING STORY

My story that I choose to drive my life is:

As you read your new story, what is the feeling you get from it? Aim for something that feels compelling, positive, expansive, and even warm or tingly inside your body. Try it on for size. Read it out loud. Imagine that this way of being already exists for you.

What thoughts and images come up for you?

Consider this new energizing story as your anchor for the rest of the book. Each time you're about to begin a new chapter, return here and read your new story out loud to ground yourself. Read and recommit to this new story daily. As you come up with more thoughts and images that reflect this story, or have experiences that illustrate this story, write them down. Start to notice how being aware of and consciously applying this new story creates change in your life.

Here's an example. Betty's old story was "People keep pulling everything out of me, leaving me nothing to give myself." Her new story became: "I'm prioritizing mutually beneficial relationships and am treating my body in ways that optimally strengthen it, so I can be at my best for myself and those important to me." Over time, focusing on this new story helped Betty retire the one-sided friendships that no longer worked for her and instill a new habit of consistently working out. Making these patterns her "new normal" led to more joy and peace, the ability to hike trails she previously shunned, and the confidence to resume dating.

What could be possible for you when you choose a new, invigorating story for yourself?

<hr>

The next chapter shows you how to build on the momentum of your new story by recognizing the strengths you bring to the table, along with the energies currently working for and against you, in making that story a reality.

CHAPTER TWO

Affirm Your Strengths and Supporting Energies

"The way you choose to see the caliber of your potential determines everything you see and every action you take in this lifetime."

~TAMA KIEVES

At times, I witness women wanting to change, but they're waiting for all the right things to come into alignment first. Waiting for the kids to go to college. Waiting to finish a project, land the next piece of business or a new job, get their finances in order, or any other life situation to complete. If there is an urge within you to elevate your current energy, I encourage you to follow that pull now – don't wait! Keeping the status quo is keeping you in the same place. Maybe you can't achieve the ideal state tomorrow, but you can start to move in that direction today. It's about making progress, not achieving perfection. Recognize that your best each day is different, depending on a variety of factors, both within and outside your control, on a given day. In the four exercises in this chapter, you'll identify what to bring forward and what to leave behind as you start making your new energizing story a reality.

A common place for folks to begin on the road to habit change is looking at weaknesses to improve. The problem? That perspective can feel uninspiring, delay forward movement, and keep us stuck in our tracks. These are all low-energy states.

Instead, let's look at the other side of the coin.

If you've lived on this planet for at least four decades, you have many valuable lessons to apply in this process of gaining more energy and vitality and burnout-proofing your life. When was the last time you stopped to consider the highlights of what you have learned, achieved and the strengths you used and honed along the way? Launching an energy- and vitality-filled life is propelled by the talents and competencies we bring to the table. I realize that (1) you may not be used to identifying your strengths and (2) you may be out of practice in prioritizing your self-care. These are the mental muscles you will incrementally build as you read this book, much as you'd use an exercise program to rebuild or tone your body's muscles. As Kay, mother of a severely handicapped adult daughter, states, "you must make time for yourself: your peace, your spirit. Get everyone around you used to that on Day One." Make today your new Day One. Each tip you use and/ or activity you perform from *Ignition* will bring you closer to igniting your energy full throttle.

EXERCISE ONE: START BEFRIENDING YOUR STRENGTHS

I view taking on changes as akin to effectively starting a new project. When you begin a new challenge, reflecting on strengths that you bring to the table helps you to hit the ground running with an empowered foundation. We can be quick to point out our own faults or perceived weaknesses, which makes it tricky to determine our assets. If that happens to be your current go-to way of thinking, I invite you to try something different, and *list your strengths*. I've suggested five possible options from which you can choose:

OPTION 1: Take the free VIA character strengths assessment online.[1] Download the character strengths profile, noting especially your top three strengths.

OPTION 2: Look back on your life and consider times where you accomplished something. It could be related to your health, wellness, energy and vitality or to a completely different part of your life. Write down your strengths that enabled those accomplishments to occur.

1 www.viacharacter.org

OPTION 3: Which of your strengths have other people commented on to you? Pay special attention to and consider those strengths that you hear about from others and for which you repeatedly receive compliments.

OPTION 4: Ask three to five people who know you well for their feedback on your strengths and ask them to give examples of you demonstrating those strengths.

OPTION 5: Use a life review to highlight your potential, bringing it front and center. Start with a blank canvas that inspires you to create. That clean slate could be your journal, a whiteboard, poster board, or any other large sheet of paper. Consider each decade of your life, one at a time. As you review each decade, document the highlights, such as milestones, areas of growth, and/or lessons learned. Also, for each decade, note the skills and talents you used in your achievements. This is no time for modesty: treat this exercise as a treasure hunt. You're uncovering and/or reminding yourself of your life's gems. Give yourself the quality time and place this historical dig deserves; it might be a few hours on a weekend at a library or other quiet place inside or outdoors. Once you complete this review, acknowledge and celebrate the strengths you've identified.

After you have identified your strengths, choose from a variety of creative ways to consciously use them and/or keep them top of mind:

- Make flash cards, one for each strength, using index cards. Pick one at the start of each day to focus on, or keep the deck handy to flip through when you're facing a challenge and need to be reminded of your strengths.
- Produce a collage of your strengths and/or images that symbolize those words.
- Create an audio recording of your strengths to play back to yourself when you need a boost or a reminder.
- Each day, set an intention to use at least one of your strengths in some way.
- Consider starting a "kudos" folder in your email or a "kudos" document on your phone and store any compliments or testimonials there.

Now that you're armed with your strengths, let's add the types of energy that you want to increase or carry forward, and what to reduce or leave behind on this trek toward energized, burnout-proof living.

EXERCISE TWO: PERFORM AN ENERGY EVALUATION

You likely have some aspects of your energy that are working well for you and others that are working against you. To self-assess your present energy state, conduct an initial Energy Evaluation. Think of this as a snapshot of what's currently giving you energy and what's depleting your energy. You can describe these as energy infusers and energy drains. Energy infusers are the activities, mindsets, fuels, conditions, types of people, attitudes and/or perspectives that generate positive energy for you. They have an aliveness that's uplifting. It doesn't necessarily mean you're perpetually bouncing off the walls: it's simply feeling positively engaged. Energy drains are the opposite – these are the beliefs, individuals, situations, responsibilities or qualities that detract from or otherwise sap your energy and vitality.

Lynne, an alternative medicine specialist I interviewed for this book, says, "The negative useless energy is soupy and thick: it can cling to you and drag you down and make you feel uninspired." Note that in assessing the energy infusers and drains in your life, the goal is not about being happy all the time. It's about deliberately using your energy in the best possible way to consistently fuel *you*. Also, as Lynne notes, it's about being "aware of how you're affecting the energy or being affected by the energy-causing situations around you."

STEP 1: Document Today's Energy Picture. Fill in the two columns of the table below with a list of the energy infusers in your life now, and a list of energy drains that currently exist for you.

ENERGY INFUSERS	ENERGY DRAINS

STEP 2: Consider Additional Energy Infusers. If you have additional ideas for other energy infusers (e.g., ways of doing or being you've used in the past, or have wanted to try), add those to the Energy Infusers column on the left.

STEP 3: Choose Your Future Energy Picture. As you review the lists you've created, step back and consider the big picture and what's important to you in your life at this time.

- What most matters to you, overall, in your life?
- What is the current priority for you, value-wise and/or achieve-ment-wise?
- Which energy infusers, if you had them consistently in your life over the next ninety days, would make the biggest difference in helping you to live congruently with your priorities, intentions and values?
- Which energy drains would be most powerful for you to diminish over the next ninety days, toward making the biggest difference in helping you to live congruently with your priorities, intentions and values?

In answering these last two questions, you might even mentally walk through the infusers and drains one at a time, imagining an infuser present now for you, and a drain gone from your life, and tune into how each one feels in your body. In each column, circle or star the top three with the larg-est impact. Make two new prioritized lists, identifying the top three infusers and drains that you feel will give you the biggest lifts, feelings of lightness, ease, and/or expansiveness in creating burnout-proof living.

Energy infusers I'm ready to consistently incorporate in my life:

1.

2.

3.

Energy drains I'm ready to reduce/eliminate from my life:

1.

2.

3.

Your infusers and drains may range across the spectrum from relatively large to quite small: music, a mindset, being outdoors, your job, clutter, a relationship. The idea of adding or removing aspects can generate a mix of feelings and emotions, from excitement to anxiety. Acknowledge what comes up for you, don't worry about the "how" for the moment; focus on why you're making these changes for yourself and the outcomes you'd like to experience.

In the next exercise, you'll claim these new energy aspects for yourself as you move on to Chapter 3.

EXERCISE THREE: BASK IN YOUR STRENGTHS AND POSITIVE ENERGIES

Imagine yourself committed to the strengths and energies you've decided to leverage as you go forward. The operative word is "decide." There are a variety of ways you can envision yourself demonstrating these traits and then keep them top of mind as you progress. Use one or more of these options now, repeating as desired through your journey.

- Meditate on your strengths, energy infusers, and releasing your energy drains.
- Journal or doodle about your strengths and energy infusers.
- Create a vision board that illustrates these concepts. You might use something like Pinterest or Instagram, or a poster board or a bulletin board using photos, words and images.

In the following final exercise for this chapter, you'll use a somatic technique (paying attention to the body's sensations and using movement) to solidify your strengths and supporting energies.

EXERCISE FOUR: FULLY ANCHOR YOUR STRENGTHS AND ENERGIES

Re-read the new energizing story you wrote in Chapter 1. Review the strengths you've identified in this chapter, the energy infusers you want to leverage, and the energy drains you're ready to release in some fashion. Wherever you are, stand up and walk to a spot where you have at least three feet of clear space in front of you. Imagine there is a line on the floor. The side of the line where you are is your life up until this moment, with all the history, baggage and old stories.

1. Step, leap or jump over the imaginary line onto the other side. Think of this as the launching pad of the newly energized life you're creating. It's a clean start to a new journey of discovery.
2. Turn around and look back at where you came from. Acknowledge the lessons you've learned, what you're leaving behind, and what you're taking with you.
3. Visualize leaving whatever you want to release in a room or building. Imagine yourself outside this room or building, and shut the door.
4. Now, face forward. Close your eyes, relax your shoulders, feel the soles of your feet touching the ground. In your mind, create a picture of yourself living with your ideal level of energy and vitality. See it, hear it, feel it. Bring a hand to your heart.
5. When you're ready, open your eyes, and if so inspired, dance in your new space to celebrate the start of this new phase for yourself. You may wish to note any thoughts, reflections, or body sensations in your journal.

You've now created the foundational pieces that help you to reset your direction. In the next chapter, I introduce a tool that will guide you through the remaining essential elements of *Ignition* and help you tailor a path that will help you elevate your energy and vitality for burnout-proof living.

CHAPTER THREE

The Burnout-Proofing Dashboard and Your Wellness Vision

"You've got to think about big things while you're doing small things, so that all the small things go in the right direction."
~ ALVIN TOFFLER

You're familiar with how your car's dashboard panel provides you with a snapshot of the vehicle's status. A quick glance furnishes information on the temperature, speed, gear in use, and fuel available. With this information, you can make informed decisions about whether to maintain the current state, make minor adjustments, fuel up or schedule a tune-up. Using that automotive metaphor, I've created the Burnout-Proofing Dashboard as a tool to:

- introduce and then help you self-assess the elements essential to igniting your energy and vitality, and
- use on an ongoing basis to monitor the quality of each of these dashboard elements as you incorporate their corresponding principles, mindsets and behaviors.

To that end, this chapter introduces the Burnout-Proofing Dashboard, powered by a Wellness Vision, and walks you through the components so you can determine the degree to which each element is currently present in your life. Once you evaluate each element's potency level, I'll direct you to the relevant chapters to read in Part Two, along with their associated exercises, tips and questions. You may choose to conduct these Part Two activities as you go, or read them first, documenting the ones you're willing to experiment with, and then fold your desired activities into the action plan you'll create in Part Three's Chapter 10 (Ignite Burnout-Proof Patterns). I suggest that you work first through those chapters covering the elements that have a lower quality rating for you right now, as it will benefit you the most to tackle these elements first. Doing so helps you customize your own path through *Ignition*, similar to what happens in a private coaching engagement. For example, if you discover you have a high level of inner balance but a low level of in-person social connection, you could start with building social outlets and contacts, as discussed in Chapter 9.

As you implement each of your selected elements (whether you do so chapter by chapter, or after you start following the action plan you'll create in Chapter 10), I encourage you to periodically revisit the Burnout-Proofing Dashboard to check in and decide what adjustments, if any, are merited. In summary, the Burnout-Proofing Dashboard provides an initial overview, directs you on your areas of focus, and is a way for you to check in and regroup for ongoing maintenance and future tweaks.

The Wellness Vision we'll develop in this chapter is what ultimately drives your new habit and behavior patterns. As the Burnout-Proofing Dashboard on page 30 illustrates, your strengths, energizing story, and energy infusers (shown at the base of the illustration) serve as the foundation for your trek. Direct your attention to the circle in the center of the four-quadrant diagram. That is your Wellness Vision, which you can think of as your destination: it ultimately describes what you're creating for your health and wellness. Surrounding the Wellness Vision is inner balance. No matter what you want to address for your health, wellness and energy, to do so optimally requires inner balance. In fact, as I mentioned in the Introduction, I advise prioritizing inner balance over work-life balance. Possessing inner balance allows you to operate from a place of being centered in feelings of calmness, peace and clarity, no matter what is occurring externally. Alternatively, if you're caught up in the outer frenzy of life, chances are the decisions you make will reflect that chaos. Use this dashboard to start your journey and to keep yourself on track while burnout-proofing your ways of being and doing as you're living.

Burnout-Proofing Dashboard

Who are you **being** and what are you **doing** to live your energizing story?

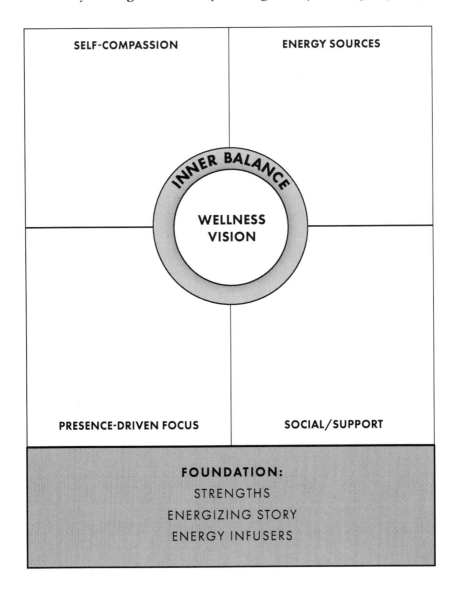

SELF-COMPASSION

ENERGY SOURCES

INNER BALANCE

WELLNESS VISION

PRESENCE-DRIVEN FOCUS

SOCIAL/SUPPORT

FOUNDATION:

STRENGTHS

ENERGIZING STORY

ENERGY INFUSERS

Contemplating Habit Changes Can Stall Us

For many, the thought of change is scary and feels hard. There's a certain comfort level in the status quo. The devil you know is better than the one you don't. That line of thinking can keep you in the same place for weeks, months, and even years longer than necessary. Not taking on different habits when you're unsatisfied with your current level of health and energy keeps you playing small. Not only do you lose out, but so do those around you. It's like cutting yourself off at the knees, stifling your power.

> *"The most common way people give up their power is thinking they don't have any."*
>
> *~ Alice Walker*

Consider what's stopping you from changing. Do you think that it feels too hard? Is there guilt around your past inability to successfully change? Do you feel guilty about or can't see how to devote the time, space and energy to change now? Afraid of failure? Unclear on where to begin? Unsure of how you'd integrate these changes into your life? In my current page-a-day calendar of Wayne Dyer thoughts, I came across this message, which felt serendipitously applicable: "As you look back on your life, know that you've failed at nothing – all you've done is produce certain results. You can view it all as what you needed to experience in order to get to a higher place."

I ask that you embrace at least test-driving some new lines of thinking. What if, as a result of embarking on change, you fly instead of fail? The truth is no one has a crystal ball. No one can guarantee the outcomes from making any changes in your life. What I can guarantee, however, is if you keep showing up to your life in the same way and follow the same routine, you're going to get the same results. If your current patterns are putting you at risk for health issues and leaving you depleted, or if you have a family history of health challenges that you're not addressing in yourself, you risk that your health quality will decrease.

Conversely, when you take on habit change with a willingness to experiment, learn and be open to thinking about, approaching and doing things differently in service to your health, you open the floodgates! You increase your potential for increased energy, as well as a freer, more engaged, awake and satisfying life. You shine, and your brightness of elevated health and wellness boosts the light in others.

Let's shelve the how-you-make-this-happen for the moment. For now, contemplate thinking and feeling differently.

Answer the following questions:

- Envision that it's some point in the future and you've attained the energy and vitality you crave. What would being consistently and steadily fueled look like to you?

- What if you embraced the idea that we are innately balanced? How would that change your approach to your health?

- What if you treated your health and wellness like an essential tool, that, when optimally tuned, allowed you to remove your blocks toward excellence and the ways you show up and serve others? What would be the impact of that choice?

Create Your Wellness Vision

Now that you've answered those questions, let's start where you are to create your own Wellness Vision. Carve out space where you can decide what's most important to you, in terms of burnout-proofing your life and choose the paths that can move you in that direction. Find a spot that's appropriate for this introspective session: somewhere in your home, outside in a garden, at a coffee shop, in a co-working space, at the library, or on a mini-retreat-for-one at a retreat center, hotel lobby, or conference room. Choose a place where you can sink into this process and give yourself the mind and heart space to bring all of yourself to this activity.

First of all, start with creating a Wellness Vision that captures the big-picture target for your energy and vitality. What does your health look like when you are living consistent with the new energizing story you created back in Chapter 1? Imagine you have the new story, and corresponding mindsets, patterns of habits and behaviors cemented in place at some point in the future (nine to twelve months out). Ponder the following questions:

- What's essential to your energy, vitality and well-being over that period of time?
- How would you feel, having attained that vision?
- When you reach this state, how would you talk to yourself and others about your life, health, energy and vitality?
- How would other people describe how they see and experience you?

Use your responses to create a descriptive, inspiring paragraph of three to five sentences with as much clarity and concreteness as you can. It might also help to pretend that someone will produce a documentary of what you have attained, and that you're writing the script. Paint as vivid a picture as you can of who you are when you reach this state: what kinds of things are you saying, thinking and feeling; what routines do you have in place; what kinds of people are with you?

Here is one example of a Wellness Vision:

I'm responding in a more conscious way to my work chaos. I'm gladly attending an enjoyable social gathering once a week. My body feels strong and vibrant from completing a 5K by at least walking or walk/jogging it. I have a routine relaxation practice in place. I feel more grounded, less flustered, less in a rush, and people often comment on my calm, positive demeanor.

WELLNESS VISION
What is your Wellness Vision?

To further anchor your Wellness Vision, answer the following questions:

1. BIG WHYS: Why take on these changes now? What is important to you about attaining this vision? Why does reaching this vision matter so much to you? What will accomplishing this vision allow or enable for you? (Answering all these questions develops your big whys – you're describing why you are taking on the pattern changes to realize your Wellness Vision.)

2. POTENTIAL OBSTACLES: What could potentially get in the way of you attaining this vision?

3. WORK-AROUNDS: What are some work-arounds for the possible roadblocks you identified in response 2?

4. TO BE AND TO FEEL: Instead of a to-do list, play with creating a to-be list and/or a to-feel list. How do you want to be in your everyday life, and how/what do you want to feel? What will help you generate that way of being and feeling in your life?

You may want to post your Wellness Vision and responses to the above questions in a place where you can review them frequently, especially while you're experimenting with and implementing the elements in the subsequent chapters.

Self-Assess Your Step-by-Step Path

Now, with your Wellness Vision established, you have a sense of direction about where you're heading. How to arrive at this vision starts with evaluating the current quality level of each essential element in the Burnout-Proofing Dashboard – giving each one a rating – so you can decide where to go next.

Looking at each of these elements for yourself, considering the level at which each one presently exists in your life, what rating would you apply to each element on a scale of 1-10, where 1 is a poor quality level and 10 is an excellent quality level?

INNER BALANCE: sense of resilience, grounding, centeredness, breathing room

☐ 1 ☐ 2 ☐ 3 ☐ 4 ☐ 5 ☐ 6 ☐ 7 ☐ 8 ☐ 9 ☐ 10

SELF-COMPASSION: being kind, patient, loving to yourself: honoring your needs

☐ 1 ☐ 2 ☐ 3 ☐ 4 ☐ 5 ☐ 6 ☐ 7 ☐ 8 ☐ 9 ☐ 10

PRESENCE-DRIVEN FOCUS: living deliberately with intention, attention and impulse control

☐ 1 ☐ 2 ☐ 3 ☐ 4 ☐ 5 ☐ 6 ☐ 7 ☐ 8 ☐ 9 ☐ 10

ENERGY SOURCES: possessing the physical, emotional, mental and/or spiritual energy required to attain your Wellness Vision

☐ 1 ☐ 2 ☐ 3 ☐ 4 ☐ 5 ☐ 6 ☐ 7 ☐ 8 ☐ 9 ☐ 10

SOCIAL/SUPPORT: having a reliable support system and in-person social connections

☐ 1 ☐ 2 ☐ 3 ☐ 4 ☐ 5 ☐ 6 ☐ 7 ☐ 8 ☐ 9 ☐ 10

If you rated any element a 5 or less, read the corresponding chapters first, in whatever order most appeals to you using the table on the next page. You might choose up to two elements to focus on first, if you're feeling especially overwhelmed. Elements rated 6 or 7 would be the next priority in your reading. Finally, since items rated 8-10 signify current strengths for you, you might read the relevant chapters at some later point to keep maintaining those qualities, or if you ever feel you need a tune-up in those areas.

ESSENTIAL ELEMENT	CHAPTER
INNER BALANCE	Chapter 4: Foster Your Inner Balance
SELF-COMPASSION	Chapter 5: Dance with Loving Acceptance and Self-Compassion
PRESENCE-DRIVEN FOCUS	Chapter 6: Practice Presence-Driven Focus
ENERGY SOURCES	Chapter 7: Play in Energized Places Chapter 8: Maximize Your Energy Intelligence
SOCIAL/SUPPORT	Chapter 9: Cultivate Relationships and Social Connections

Consider the chapters listed in this table as stand-alone entities. You will discover some overlap and cross-referencing between chapters, for particular aspects you might explore in further depth. Some chapters have numbered and named exercises, others have questions, checklists or tables woven into the content. As you read each chapter you've chosen (corresponding with the elements you want to strengthen), you will select the patterns you want to bring forth into this way of being and doing that creates your Wellness Vision and is aligned with your new energizing story. In a sense, you're crafting a customized step-by-step hike on your own unique journey, beginning with your strengths and an empty metaphorical backpack. Initially, the empty backpack signifies that you are starting open and clean: you're leaving behind what doesn't support your future mode of operating. The backpack provides a repository for collecting the new ways of being and doing that you will put into practice. You will cherry-pick the elements that, at a minimum, you're open to experimenting with as part of a ninety-day action plan that you'll later create in Chapter 10. You may even elect to start testing these elements as you read each chapter you've selected and/or document your choices in Chapter 10's building blocks on pages 122 through 126 – that's also part of customizing your unique path and figuring out your energizing burnout-proof rhythm.

Choosing or playing with the new patterns as you're reading doesn't mean you're cementing them in your life; it just indicates that you're at least open to trying them on because you're curious to experience the effect on your energy and vitality. Consider the tips and exercises in Chapters 4-9 as a buffet from which to sample: select those you are drawn to, intrigued by, or maybe even ones that initially appear distasteful to you.

Let's get started! It's time to move on to the first chapter you selected.

Part Two:
Cruise Pathways of Doing and Being

CHAPTER FOUR

Foster Your Inner Balance

"Stop trying to make sanity out of an insane situation.
If your schedule is crazy busy, you don't need time management, you
need space."
~ CHERYL RICHARDSON

You can think of inner balance as recognizing and operating from the quiet space within that exists perpetually. A place of power, wisdom, and peace. Just as a solid and stable physical core helps us in our bodily strength, paying attention to and cultivating our inner core assists our resiliency and ability to move in an engaged, energetic fashion through life. Think of it as inner space to play with in creating vitality. Space for your well-being. Space to take you off the constant hamster wheel. Space to think. Be. Process. Accept.

Different levels and layers of such space exist and are catalogued in this chapter. All strengthen your ability to lead yourself without solely relying on brain-power, and provide relief by giving yourself breathing room, literally and metaphorically. Further, noticing and leveraging these spaces helps increase your ability to be present (a topic further discussed in Chapter 6). Don't wait for someone to give you these spaces: stand up and grant them to yourself.

When you consciously and routinely use these spaces, beyond weekends and vacations, to give yourself inner balance, it helps you to be the calm in the storm, and find respite in what can sometimes feel like the chaos of life. This is why I feel so strongly about prioritizing inner balance over work-life balance. When we are able to function and make decisions from a place of inner peace, that energy and clarity ripples out in how we show up to others, the actions and words we use, and the perspectives we hold.

At first blush, the notion of space can seem like a luxury for anyone functioning on chronic autopilot. Feeling like we're on the never-ending hamster wheel of to-dos, activities, and responsibilities. Being a slave to our phones.

Here's a news flash: we're not robots. We're human *beings*, not human doings.

Consider the following types of spaces to spark your thinking in this area. Put a check mark beside those that intrigue you as you read the descriptions. What might it be like for you to come from an inner place of ease instead of pushing?

☐ **INNER SPACE:** The space within furnishes a grounded-ness and clear connection to your essence, giving yourself the opportunity to hear, recall and embrace it. Here, "it" is your soul, heart, intuition, and/or connection to Source. When you're able to dwell in this endless space, you get out of the noise and into the peace that always exists. You hear, see and remember Truth. The awareness of this space and connecting to it often is the ultimate in acknowledging that you are not alone. For example, as I'm writing this book, I'm using "Remembrance" practices that I learned in Mark Silver's "Heart of Business" course to be in relationship with not only my own heart, but the heart of my business and this book. It is mentally and spiritually opening to consider that everything has a heart, and we can connect with our hearts to communicate, ask for what we need, and replenish the qualities that help us flourish and thrive. We don't need to depend on only our human selves: there is an infinite supply of loving guidance always available. We just need to stop long enough to listen to this eternal wisdom.

☐ **THE SPACE OF DISTANCE:** This is the space in which you can step back: to reassess, plan, refocus, regroup. When we're constantly living in the weeds, it's challenging to see a different way of being and possibilities. Giving ourselves a periodic 50,000-foot view can open the door to new and different options. Think of it as a check-in: evaluating whether this is still the track we want to be on, or whether how we're doing and being is taking us closer to or moving us further away from the intended destination. Planning with distance takes a big-picture approach: not only the action steps needed, but how we best fuel ourselves to perform those action steps, the support we need, and the environmental factors that help and hamper us.

By "environmental," I mean how you set up or structure your home or work environment to support (versus hinder) you, to keep what's important top of mind, inspire you, remind you of your big whys, and furnish a setting aligned with what you're creating. When we find that we've strayed from or are stumbling along the path, it's good to allow ourselves the space to refocus and regroup instead of pressing forward. Every so often we need to pop up from being submerged.

You can also look at this as the space between you the observer and you the human being. This is how Eckhart Tolle describes one aspect of what he calls "Presence." The watcher, one who sees, moving out of thought and ego. You can create this distance in any doing or being activity, at multiple points of the day. When you find yourself mentally approaching an activity as a means to an end or something to "get through," instead consciously embrace, align and be in harmony with the journey that is this moment. (This element of space is like stepping out of your own perspective to observe yourself as a neutral third party might. You could even imagine your current life situation playing on a movie screen, with you sitting in the theater watching as it's happening.)

☐ **PHYSICAL AND VISUAL SPACE:** At my hair salon, I once encountered an agile elderly female client who professed the importance of getting outside every day, even in the blizzards that can occur during New England winters. She lives in an apartment building, and at a bare minimum, every day, even during severe or inclement weather, if she's not able to safely walk outdoors, she steps outside the front door of her apartment building to get some fresh air. Getting outside reminds us of the space that surrounds us, the unending sky, and our relative place in the world. I'm reminded of the scene from the movie *Shawshank Redemption*, just after Andy escapes from prison, and the infinite joy in his face and entire body expression when he stands up in the middle of a river, in the dark of night and pouring rain, staring up to the heavens, arms extended in celebrating his victory.

You can also feel more expansive and open by noting the visual space in a photo, painting, sculpture, or even the architecture of buildings. Observe the dance of nature, people, animals and human creations as we move through the world – whether we're driving, biking, running or walking. Observe the spaces between homes, individuals, vehicles, trees, leaves and branches on the trees, petals on flowers, insects, and blades of grass. Such space is woven all around us. When you're sufficiently awake to see the spaces in nature, art, or other human-made creations, it increases your awareness of the nooks of space available within you, especially at times where you're feeling squeezed.

☐ **AUDITORY SPACE:** Spoken or sung words and musical notes are each surrounded by space. One could contend that it's the space that makes the words or notes appear. If you pay close attention, you can hear the periodic inhale between words and, for wind instruments, between the notes. In conversation, how much space are you allowing between the end of another person's sentence and the time when you respond? Are you allowing enough space to truly *hear* them (vs. preparing your response as they're speaking)? Notice what's being said, what's not being said, and the energy in their tone and pace of speech.

☐ **BODY SPACE:** There is an inner and outer aspect to this element. The life energy within your body is always there and functioning without needing input from you (e.g., brain activity, heartbeat, blood pumping, lungs expanding and contracting, nails growing). Reminding yourself of that space can help ground you. The outer aspect is the space you take up with your body. How are you moving through the world? What are your pace, stance and posture like? Are you moving through gracefully or clumsily? Are you rushed or easeful? Rough or smooth? Stepping lightly or plowing through? What is the body language you show when you speak? What about when you listen? If you're not sure, start observing or ask a trusted friend for feedback.

☐ **SPACE TO ALLOW/ACCEPT:** This is the intellectual space of being with *what is.* Not necessarily one of condoning or approval: simply acknowledging that in this moment, this is the current reality. No story, interpretation or judgment. Just the bare facts. The clarity and energy of allowing or accepting paves the way for consciously choosing your next step.

☐ **SPACE TO NOTICE (BEFORE OUTWARDLY RESPONDING):** Your body is a wise organ. It not only responds to the food and beverages you supply it, and the sleep you give it, it reacts to external stimuli such as life situations and others' words. Giving yourself the space to notice thoughts running through your head, emotions that bubble up, feelings that arise, and body sensations (heart pounding, jaw clenching, stomach aching), can help you artfully and consciously respond instead of impulsively react.

☐ **JOY SPACE:** Routinely inject joy and/or good adrenaline into your life. Protect and carve out a space for goofiness, fun, intimacy, pleasure, and laughter. While coaching Maria – a married mother in her early forties with two young adult children – I got the sense that, among her and her husband's jobs and outside commitments, joy space hadn't been part of the picture. When I checked my suspicions by asking Maria when she last had a "date night" out with her husband, she confirmed they had tossed the idea around for a while, but all they'd managed so far were weekly movies at home. If joy space is currently absent for you, or you've been only *thinking* about fun things, move into action on this one. Ideas include spending time in sunlight or nature, going for a run, meditating, visiting an art gallery. Many of us have forgotten what makes our heart sing. Remind yourself with a frequent shot of joy.

☐ **QUIET/DISCONNECT SPACE:** Life can get noisy, our senses can be on overdrive, and we can feel pulled in a million directions at once. The respite of quiet moments can be our savior. Whether you sit in silence, contemplation, or devotion matters less than whether you take yourself out of the day-to-day grind and build in conscious, deliberate moments of peace. You can create these moments after work, in between appointments or tasks, shuttling the kids around, or during an afternoon break. Disconnect in a way that works for you. Shut off the phone, make a cup of tea, close your eyes and just sit in the stillness. Hide in the bathroom if you have to! We each deserve (and function better with) daily moments of peace.

☐ **SPACE THAT YOU INHABIT:** What energy are you radiating into the space around you? What are you allowing into your space? What are you carrying with you? What needs to be released? The following personal example from Cindy illustrates several of these aspects.

Cindy, a registered nurse in her late forties, has a side business of doing Reiki, psychic readings, spiritual tunings and mediumship. What she learned in going through her spiritual training is that she is an empath, in that she absorbs other people's energy. Her spiritual development taught her a variety of ways to block and deflect energy. For instance, she can put a bubble around herself in a metaphysical sense, to not take on someone else's energy and instead give it back to them while still being empathetic to their situation. This technique allows her to protect herself from absorbing another person's negative energy. If she's feeling especially drained on some days, she does a quick meditation visualizing a power cord attached to the sun and lets the sun's energy re-energize her. This approach improves the energy she both carries and emanates in her space.

Today, in her nursing role full-time, working with veterans in a primary care clinic, and living with both rheumatoid arthritis and fibromyalgia, she finds managing her energy to be a day-to-day struggle, as she's constantly dealing with the external situations of patient behaviors. She's had angry patients yelling and swearing at her, for example. She copes with such stressful triggers in several ways:

- Walking by the river outside her workplace,
- Going outside and literally shaking herself off,
- Doing deep breathing exercises that calm and center her, and
- Telling herself to let it go when the stress wells up.

On the last point, she knows her stress threshold has been crossed when she hears the "Let It Go" song from the movie *Frozen* playing in her head. She takes that as her cue to step back and use any of the above techniques to release negative vibes from her space.

Two months ago, she broke up with her fiancé of five years, since he was, as she puts it, an "energy sapper." While they were best friends, he didn't support her in pursuing her metaphysical work, or in the household chores. This circumstance was bringing her energy down. Her head is already in a better place, and she feels there is less external negative energy being emitted from her.

☐ **"SHOWER" SPACE:** Admit it, you've had them: those experiences in the shower where ideas and solutions pop into your head from out of nowhere. Earlier, you may have been absorbed in a task or problem and hit a mental impasse. The shower time furnishes the physical and energetic distance from the issue at hand, taking your mind away from that burrowing focus. It's a place in which your mind can run free with no boundaries. Some folks create this same sensation by taking a walk or going for a run. It may seem counterintuitive, but pushing to force an answer doesn't always work.

☐ **SPACE TO MOVE/RELEASE:** We have become overly sedentary in our lives, as the headlines continue to warn. Some researchers have gone as far as saying that sitting is the new smoking! We spend too much time sitting at our desks or dining tables, commuting in vehicles, planting ourselves on the couch for hours in front of our screen of choice. Ergotron, a company that makes ergonomic products for improved workplace productivity, says on their juststand.org website that the amount of time the average person is sitting down (aka sedentary) each day is 12 hours.

Adults in the United States devoted about 10 hours and 39 minutes each day to consuming media during the first quarter of 2016, according to a Nielsen Company audience report.[1] That number increased by thirty minutes in 2017[2] which is close to an eMarketer forecast.[3] Here, "media" includes our tablets, smartphones, personal computers, video games, radios, DVD players, DVRs and TVs.

To counter all this immobility, build pockets of movement and release into your day. Start with taking breaks where you get up and move around at certain intervals, if you're sitting for an extended period of time. When you take a lunch break, really treat it as a break. Eat somewhere other than your desk or office. Take a walk. If you can't do either, shut off your computer monitor and speakers, and let calls go to voicemail during your break.

Release can take the form of a walk, run, workout, stretch, a dance, or a moving meditation. (A moving meditation is one where you basically move in ways you feel drawn to move, beginning from a standing position. Stretch, angle, bend and twist parts of your body in all directions.) You can strategically use movement and/or release between transitions, such as after a challenging conversation or to clear the deck before a situation that requires a high level of focus and engagement.

1 www.cnn.com/2016/06/30/health/americans-screen-time-nielsen/index.html
2 www.nielsen.com/us/en/insights/reports/2017/the-nielsen-total-audience-q2-2017.html
3 www.emarketer.com/Article/US-Adults-Now-Spend-12-Hours-7-Minutes-Day-Consuming-Media/1015775

☐ **SPACE GAINED BY RELEASING OTHERS:** Here, I don't necessarily mean releasing other people wholesale from your life, although that could be an option for people who are detrimental to your energy (as Cindy did with her fiancé in the example earlier in this chapter). This is more about encouraging others to grow by scaling back their dependence on you and regaining some space for yourself. One example is grooming your growing children to take on more age-appropriate responsibility and become more self-sufficient. It doesn't mean you take away your love, care and concern for them; you just demonstrate it in different ways. Or, if you're in a leadership position at work, empower others to succeed without micro-managing them. Give them general tools, clear standards, guidance and ground rules, and set them on their way while still conveying that you are there when they need support.

☐ **CALENDAR SPACE:** If you look at your calendar now, how much open space do you see? If you're booked or overcommitted with back-to-back appointments and responsibilities, that can make it feel impossible to find breathing room for inner stillness. Reevaluate what's working for you and against you, in moving toward burnout-proof living. What can be pared back, peeled off or done differently to free up more of your space? For an in-depth look at what belongs on your plate now, follow the recommendations supplied by author Greg McKeown in his book *Essentialism*. McKeown describes ways to focus your time and energy, as he puts it, on the "vital few" versus the "trivial many." Also avoid immediately jamming in additional to-do activities when you're gifted with "found space" from tasks or appointments taking less time than you expected or when you get a cancellation. If the potential options for creating gaps are not obvious to you at the moment, explore the presence principles in Chapter 6 to build your attention muscles and see possible choices. Further, the exercises and personal examples in other Part Two chapters may give you other ideas.

☐ **PHONE-FREE SPACE:** Similar to calendar space, look at ways to free yourself of chronic phone viewing, especially when you're waiting – in a doctor's office, in a checkout line, or for someone to show up to an appointment. Are you always looking at your phone during a meal, walking, watching a sporting event, or using public transportation? Instead of always automatically reaching for your phone when gaps arise, welcome phone-free space. Notice your surroundings. Land in your body. Reconnect with all your senses. Practice being okay with simply being. Give yourself such gaps in the morning and evening as well. Instead of picking up your phone first thing in the morning, start with a routine that lets you reconnect within, establishes your priority for the day, and sets your day up for success. Have a cutoff time in the evening where you stop phone use until the next morning.

☐ **SPACE FOR HOW YOU'RE FEELING (AND YOUR REACTION TO HOW YOU'RE FEELING):** Feelings and emotions, positive or negative, are part of what makes us human. I've encountered countless examples of people dismissing, submerging or ignoring these feelings, whether they're celebratory, crushed, or anything in between. When we allow for the space to experience those feelings, however we respond to them, that's what helps us move through, learn and grow from them.

〜〜〜〜〜〜〜〜〜〜〜

Which types of space described in this chapter resonated for you? Before you move on to the next chapter you've chosen, review your Wellness Vision and new energizing story again. Get your metaphorical backpack out and choose one to three space types that you feel will most help you to attain inner balance while moving toward your vision and living the reality of your new story.

1.

2.

3.

CHAPTER FIVE

Dance with Loving Acceptance and Self-Compassion

"True courage comes not just from feeling confident and strong, but from being the honest, authentic expression of yourself."

~ DEBBIE FORD

We women can be so incredibly hard on ourselves. How we treat ourselves, and the words we use when we talk about or to ourselves, not only in our everyday lives, but especially when we attempt to make changes for our betterment. We can be our own worst critics and enemies. Instead, let's take steps to be and accept who we are, deeply, so we can ignite oodles of good energy and release the weights that can burn us out and hold us back from attaining what is important to us. Let me share some stories that illustrate this principle.

Amanda is a two-time breast cancer survivor. When she was diagnosed the second time, it was painful and she was stressed and very anxious. The first time it was pre-cancerous stage 0, non-invasive. The second time, three or four years later, it was invasive, plus she was diagnosed with the BRCA2 gene mutation. The latter diagnosis meant she was prone to ovarian cancer and had twice the chance of getting pancreatic cancer. As part of her treatment, she opted for a double mastectomy (and later reconstruction), and having an oophorectomy (both ovaries removed). When others in her circle learned of the second diagnosis, she dealt head-on with several of society's perceived rules on how to cope with cancer. She received advice from others like "be brave," "you can handle it," "be strong," and "fight this battle." While, understandably, people were trying to be helpful, such remarks felt judgmental to Amanda at the time. She wondered, "So if I do die from this, does that mean I'm not strong enough?" When people would say things like, "You're going to be okay," her response would be, "How do you know?" She didn't want to buy into society's pressure.

Dealing with a variety of emotions – sad some days, angry other days – felt all-consuming. What gradually cemented for Amanda is that "nobody knows better than I do about what I need emotionally and spiritually, because I'm the only one feeling it. This was my unique experience, and I wanted to honor that, instead of conforming to societal norms." She realized a lot of how she felt was connected to her husband. He thought he needed to "be brave for her," and was one of the people trying to convince her that she'd be fine. Amanda realized that he and her close friends wanted her to be a certain way, so *they could feel better* about her feeling better.

When she received the second diagnosis, Amanda deeply respected what she was feeling. She knew what to expect from the medical system, knew the doctors, had a medical team that she liked and would help her, having done all that due diligence during her first cancer experience. As such, her energy was now freed up for how to look after herself, instead of looking after her husband. She managed her two children (in their teens at the second diagnosis) less than she managed her husband. In a sense, she had to train him on how to best support her. For example, on a day she felt sad, she needed lots of hugs. She asked him not to tell her to be brave, as she didn't feel brave. Him simply *being there* for her gave her strength. She needed to feel and convey her feelings to those around her.

Amanda obtained additional assistance through therapy, monthly support groups and two to three visits each week to a healing garden. The social workers in the support group (through her hospital) helped participants see what they were feeling about the journey, not just what they were doing. She found that to be an uplifting experience, as group members wanted to feel like they had hope. She was hooked on the healing garden in Harvard, Massachusetts, when she first saw it. This particular site offered beauty and peacefulness through nature walks, books, restorative space, groups, and sound healing.

As Amanda looks back on that experience, she's proud of the energy she crafted and knows that the undertaking changed her. "I honor where I am so much more. I work out why I'm not feeling great, then I inhabit that space and accept it. I feel much more grounded in respecting the space I'm in. It allows me to create the energy I need. If I'm dumping on myself, there's no space there. I'm much more willing to know what I want and advocate for it, and I'm not caring so much about what others think."

Sally had a similar discovery when she lost three pregnancies over the course of eighteen months, between giving birth to her two children. This was compounded by her mother's death two months after her first child was born; her mother had been diagnosed with cancer a few months prior to Sally's son's birth. Rather than being available to hear people's words of sympathy and attempts to help, Sally chose to retreat, or as she puts it, "go dark." Not dark in terms of depression, but off the grid and being inaccessible. As she puts it, "When I get depleted, there is so little inside for me to give to other people. I didn't have it in me. I didn't initiate much for a good amount of time." She knows herself well enough to recognize that she doesn't initially understand her feelings about such circumstances. She needs time to process. Once she figures it out, then she can come out, and, as she puts it, "rise" (get back to normal and not get stuck).

People's attempts to help Sally with words and food felt crushing to her, like a big wave in the ocean crashing down on her. An innate nurturer, she realized she needed to work on her pain instead of make someone else feel better through feeling sorry for her. For Sally, the latter took lots of emotional energy away from her. What helped her get through those losses was an ultimate feeling that she and her husband would get it right. She's held that outlook for as long as she can remember: trying to be positive, and holding the perspective that there's always a chance that things will go right. Considering the options, she says, "I hope I'm always able to rise."

The courage that both Amanda and Sally demonstrated was the openness and willingness to love and have compassion for themselves on their own terms. That meant honoring and voicing their needs, turning inward, and feeding their souls with the nourishment that they craved. Once each woman clarified her needs, she could better articulate how her family, friends and others in her network could best support them.

If you haven't experienced a crisis like Amanda or Sally, you have likely witnessed recurring themes of uncertainty, change, and lack of control through the news media and conversations with others. You may even have experienced stress surrounding one or more of those situations.

The future is unpredictable. As we increase our awareness of and note the frequency of life, work and world changes, our attention is heightened and focused on the multiple facets of life that are temporary and not set in stone, not black and white, not absolute.

Many keep banging their heads against the wall, wishing for more certainty, control, and/or knowing.

There's a better way ... dance with it. Just as Amanda and Sally danced with their adversities, you can dance with everyday life.

Think of dance not as a structured, planned set of steps or an unvarying routine. Instead, think of it as an outlook for being in the rhythm of life's flow. Think of a toddler who spontaneously dances, whether or not music is on. Think of how you intuitively move your body to a song on the dance floor, or gyrate to music in your car. Bring a sense of experimentation, play, curiosity and discovery to the task in front of you. Even if something feels challenging, bring graceful ease to it.

This is how Robyn has ultimately chosen to approach the life phase of menopause, which she is currently five years into, in her mid-fifties. As Robyn says, "No one prepares you for how menopause will affect your body. If I had built a stronger connection to taking care of myself at forty, I wouldn't be dealing with as many health challenges in my life now. During a time of financial juggling, the expenses for my self-care practices were the first to go: I didn't advocate for what I needed to keep myself physically and mentally fit. In hindsight, I realize this was the beginning of an unhealthy cycle that lasted many years. If I could speak to my younger self at forty, I'd say to put my self-care on a calendar and do not underestimate the power of honoring your true needs. Nothing is more important than your health. If I had done this, I know I could have spared myself many downward spirals."

For Robyn, those downward spirals included incremental weight gain resulting in her being forty pounds overweight, a shoulder injury from being exceedingly competitive, a return of asthma symptoms, and depression.

After in-depth introspection while she was sidelined post-injury, Robyn realized that how she physically treated herself (whether in excess activity or doing nothing) affected her emotional state, which impacted her overall energy. She needed to make adjustments to get herself out of the vicious cycle of competitive activity > injury > getting taken off track. The big shift came when Robyn stopped looking at being healthy as an outward-focused competition, and began listening to the compassionate voice inside. Today, self-love, meditation and yoga are big parts of creating an inward-focused presence, where her actions are driven from the heart instead of the mind. When she functions this way, there's no competition, she listens more effectively, she's in a state of receiving, and she's in a flow where she's connected to bringing all her energy to the situation. This new kind of "high" is helping her to move through and accept change.

Robyn now knows that every stage of our life is powerful. Moving into the next stage requires a lot of work as it is, and even more so when you're trying to avoid burning out in the process. Life stage shifts work optimally when you're not pushing or fighting against them, but instead when you understand what constitutes the best you can be through this change (while reminding yourself that your "best" may look different each day).

Ultimately, Robyn has found menopause to be a process of listening to her body and trying different approaches to see what feels right. Every other life stage has felt more clear-cut to her in terms of its predictability or knowing what to expect. But now, she is responding to the needs from her heart.

Beyond the examples cited in this chapter, you can apply the model of dancing with the rhythm and ebbs and flows of life to a variety of life situations. Think of yourself as a leaf dancing in the wind in circumstances like the following.

- unpredictable work environment
- job transition/job search
- being a caregiver
- dealing with the "long goodbye" (a loved one's decline due to illness)
- processing grief after a loss
- a personal, professional, or creative challenge
- a new approach to structuring your day

- adopting new habits that influence and improve your well-being
- spending holidays with family
- a conversation
- a relationship

When you dance, a sense of rigidity is absent. Instead, you're open to trying different approaches, tweaking as you go. Adjusting and re-adjusting. Try one set of dance steps, see what that outcome brings, and modify as needed.

I'm not encouraging you to "dance around," as in avoidance. I mean dancing as moving with the ups and downs of change, rather than fighting or resisting them. When I talk about bringing a sense of play to dance, I don't mean that the situation will always be blissfully joyful. I'm simply encouraging you to be light and exploratory about what you bring to the circumstance. Use the following exercise to allow nature to be your teacher.

EXERCISE ONE: WATCH THE DANCE OF NATURE

Sit in a natural setting for a spell and watch:

- how birds fly and then switch direction,
- how the trees bend with the wind,
- how the clouds shift and alter their formation,
- how different animals move, and
- how the waves flow over rocks and change the shoreline.

Each of these situations offers an example of accepting the current environment and readjusting responses moment to moment. (The added bonus: it's a picturesque way to have some quiet downtime for yourself.) What elements of nature's dance can you bring to your life today?

Start to think in terms of nourishing and being kind to yourself. What fuels and renews you? What feeds your soul? If you were your own best friend, how would you treat yourself right now? What words will you use to uplift when you're about to tear yourself down?

In this next exercise, if you're not used to giving yourself compassion, this meditation lays the groundwork for you to bring that way of being into place.

EXERCISE TWO: PERFORM A LOVING-KINDNESS (METTA) MEDITATION

If you're not used to being kind to yourself, conducting a loving-kindness or metta meditation is one way to begin. What's especially powerful about this form of meditation is that not only do you direct well-wishes toward yourself, you also direct them toward others. However, you start the practice with yourself. Sit in a comfortable and tranquil way, settle in and observe several in and out breaths, then mentally recite the following phrases:

- *May I be happy.*
- *May I be well.*
- *May I be safe.*
- *May I be peaceful and at ease.*

Feelings and emotions might arise as you sit with these words. Stay with them and repeat the phrases. You could even mentally picture yourself while doing so.

After some time of being in this space, now consider someone who has supported you, and mentally recite the same phrases, directing them toward that person. For example: *May you be happy. May you be well*, etc. Be with whatever feelings and emotions that come up for you.

You can then transition to meditating about people who've pushed your buttons or with whom you've had challenges, and either mentally recite the above phrases toward them, or direct loving-kindness to them in another way that feels appropriate.

Consider the mindset presented in the next exercise as a "coat" to try on while exploring the principles in this chapter.

EXERCISE THREE: ACCEPTING YOURSELF AS A BLESSING

Imagine you are a blessing. Not in a boastful way, but simply accepting that idea outright as an innate principle that exists for you and all humans. You are a blessing, period. How would that change how you:

- Live each day?
- Talk to yourself?
- Treat and nourish yourself?

Journal and/or meditate on those ideas. Watch this Louis Schwartzberg TEDxSF video, "Nature. Beauty, Gratitude."[1] (or another inspiring video) to put you in this blessed state of mind.

As you contemplate yourself as a blessing and start to dance with life in ways that bring kindness and compassion to yourself, consider what it now means to nourish yourself. Food is certainly one piece of that, and we explore that further in Chapter 8.

At another level of depth, nourishment is how you're feeding your soul. What inspires you? Use the next exercise to explore inspirational paths.

EXERCISE FOUR: IDENTIFY SOURCES OF INSPIRATION

Look to the creative realm for pointers here: art, movies, memoirs, songs, poems, spiritual or religious books, a TED talk or other compelling speech, podcast or interview, a story of overcoming adversity. What nurtures your spirit? What makes you come alive? What engages your senses? If you don't know, play with some options. What are you curious about? What calls to you or where do you feel pulled? You might even read the Spiritual Energy section in Chapter 7 to get more ideas.

Awaken your soul. Whatever was sparked for you in the previous paragraph, choose a way to stir up your creative side and test out that element.

When you reconnect with your soul, and live in a heart-led compassionate way, you start to recognize that you are not alone in whatever you are pursuing. By nurturing your spirit, you can leverage that in your chosen quest. Breathe. Imagine the pressure being lifted from your shoulders. There's no need to take all your perceived burdens solely on yourself. No need to be the hero or martyr. You have an infinite universal spiritual realm available to you, waiting to be of assistance.

～～～～～～～～～

Review your energizing story and your Wellness Vision. What aspects of self-love, compassion, and acceptance for yourself will you weave into this process to stoke your energetic fire and ward off burnout? Which exercises attract you?

1 www.ted.com/talks/louie_schwartzberg_nature_beauty_gratitude

CHAPTER SIX

Practice Presence-Driven Focus

"Stay present, alert, connected with the power of Now and the power of awareness, which is who you truly are."

~ ECKHART TOLLE

Cultivating our capacity to be present with what's here and what's now connects us to that perpetual Light within that is available to us. You may call it intuition, inner wisdom, God, Spirit, higher self, universal energy, or inner balance (as in Chapter 4). While it's always there, our mind and/or ego can block it out, in either the frenzy of our lives, or thinking we know better. One of the casualties of "busy-ness" and perpetually running on autopilot is tuning out our bodies and our feelings. Forgoing, even silencing, the heart and intuition. An over-eagerness to fill any discovered gaps in our day with more to-dos on the list, instead of savoring the "being-ness" opportunity of that space.

Our ability to practice presence grants us a path to what's real, to focus on what matters, a wider lens and a larger pool of options for functioning, and a means to pull ourselves out of the "energy ditch" of operating in a scattered, reactionary manner.

Being fully present allows you to take advantage of and re-engage all your senses. Doing so resets the energetic playing field. It helps you see what's here now and opens up more avenues for increasing your vitality. It peels away the outer layers of various life situations, reveals the authentic you underneath, and provides a clearer connection with universal energy. It's "Seeing" with a capital "S"!

"Breathe and don't abandon your body." Hearing this statement during yoga teacher training was profound for Kim, who had previously been working in public radio reporting and announcing. A panic attack on the air was the wake-up call that sent Kim on a healing journey, during which she tried every healing modality she found, including psychotherapy and Al-Anon.

Even as she stayed at her job for a while, Kim made her own healing and recovery her priority "occupation." A huge part of that process was Julia Cameron's book, *The Artist's Way*, and the daily writing ritual Cameron calls "morning pages," which helped Kim get clear that it was time to leave her job. That bold move set her on a discovery path where she continued to take leaps of faith and show up to what life presented to her. As Kim puts it, she kept following the "yesses": learning to run decisions through her body and feel the answers. A contracted feeling meant no, while an expanded feeling was a yes. Today, Kim works as a life and career coach, helping clients arrive at their own truths using these same tools and processes.

Jeri has always known she was the master of her destiny. Attracted to personal development trainings in her twenties, hearing messages of being responsible for what you say, your attitude and, overall, yourself, resonated for her. Inspired by those lessons, she chose to be self-employed, creating her own floral design business. When she got married at age thirty-five, she had already been in business for seven years. Now in her early fifties, her motto is "F*$% it, I'm fifty." She has enough life experience to avoid getting caught up in the negative energy of drama. As she says, "I can't be bothered – don't have the time or inclination." She has been practicing yoga for sixteen years and feels it's the answer to everything, in terms of what it does for her body and the breathing that keeps her centered and focused. One of the appealing aspects of the yoga studio she uses is that they do not have mirrors on the walls. It's to reinforce their message of "focus on your mat" – it's not about how people around you are doing and it's not about judging yourself. It's about honing *your* edge, your personal best. What are you doing today? There are so many distractions out there. All you can control is you. Embrace the notion that everyone has different strengths and what they can do well.

Tess applied strong intentions in deciding on the number of kids she and her husband would hope to have. Having three children felt like they could still hold onto their individual interests, allowing her to balance mother-hood and a sense of self. The thought of increasing to four made Tess feel like she'd need to be a full-time stay-at-home mom, with no additional activities and relationships. This was because of what she had observed about her parents' experience: they had no common interests, not many friends, and no strong connections in their community. Not wanting to repeat that cycle, she spent a lot of time considering what kind of family and marriage she wanted to craft, being keenly aware of the need for couples to work on their marriage when they have children. Tess had a babysitter booked every other weekend, so she and her husband could do things together, and she always made sure to have a backup babysitter available.

Over the years, Tess has developed shared hobbies with her husband, believing that "it's so much easier in marriage if you get out and play." They both love to ski, they ride bikes together, and each learned to play golf. As a fitness instructor and personal trainer, Tess often advises her clients to find things they like to do, even choosing things that they might first find uncomfortable, just because they attract you in some way. For example, she took ukulele lessons simply because it was something she was interested in learning. She loves going to Mass, as she gets a lot out of that ritual. She finds in her life, and in her clients' lives, that if we're led only by what we feel are "supposed to's," we can fall out of energy balance.

Deb started a transcendental meditation (TM) practice two years ago. She had performed meditation off and on for roughly ten years, experimenting with various practices. She wanted an anchor, but not something too complex. A certified TM teacher delivers this training, which includes taking a TM course for a couple hours a day for four consecutive days, during which you get a mantra just for you. Deb is now at the point where she can't imagine not having a practice and envisions she will meditate for the rest of her life. For her, it's grounding and it connects her to herself, something bigger, a larger perspective, and a place of gratitude, acceptance, and recognition of the perfection of the present. Her mind shifted from "should meditate" to seeing meditation as a self-honoring practice. As Deb says, "if I want to be deliberate in the world, I'd better start with myself." Indeed.

The Presence Triad

Consider the triad of principles that, used together, help us achieve presence: intention, purposeful attention (mindfulness), and impulse control.

- **INTENTION** is consciously choosing a desired outcome or direction. Taking action or being in a way that lends itself toward that end while fully alert and awake. For starters, think about how you approach your career or job, a particular role, your day, a conversation with someone, a goal you have set, and the level of intention you bring to those circumstances.

- **PURPOSEFUL ATTENTION**, or mindfulness, is noticing and observing what's going on both outside and inside you, on purpose, in the present moment, releasing immediate (and perhaps habitual) judgment. Think of toddlers exploring a new place: they are blank slates, balls of curiosity. They have no expectations; they're just seeing and noting what's around them. Mindfulness means choosing to observe what's happening outside, plus what's coming up for you inside: the thoughts that arise in your head, the emotions that churn, and the feelings that show up in your body.

- **IMPULSE CONTROL** is avoiding a knee-jerk reaction to the situation around you. By creating space between the trigger and your response, you can proceed in an intentional way. You can also view this as functioning in this moment in a way that doesn't compromise the next moment. It's being present to what is and having the ability to respond to life from a state of "now" instead of from a place of conditioned past default reactions.

Being able to tune into your body's energy and aliveness helps you to cultivate presence. You can build this muscle when you're standing in line, sitting in a doctor's waiting room, or keeping your attention focused in a group or one-on-one meeting. You can apply these concepts in any situation, positive or negative, work or non-work related. It opens the door for you to better see what you need, in the moment, for your energy and vitality.

Key Lessons in Presence

Allow me to share a personal story where I used the full triad, and learned several lessons on living in presence.

On an August morning in 2013, my husband Peter had an accident while using a table saw. It was a tool he'd used a million times over the prior twenty years. He was building a shed in our backyard. In fact, he had finished the shed, and he was just cutting the PVC trim for the door. While he doesn't know exactly what happened, his left hand either slipped or somehow got caught. The result is he lost two fingers (ring and middle), half his index finger and two-thirds of his thumb.

I wasn't home when this occurred. Luckily, we live in an urban area with houses close together, and several neighbors heard Peter's shouts for help. Someone called 911, another person ran over with a tourniquet, and another person called me.

I rushed home to see the ambulance pulling away at the end of our street, and neighbors graciously cleaning up our driveway, asking me where they could move his tools, offering me a ride to the hospital. At that point, I didn't exactly know what had happened and neither did my neighbors, only that Peter had experienced an accident with the saw. I nearly passed out as I was taking everything in – things started spinning, and I was swaying, so I sat down on the ground to compose myself. After sitting for a few minutes and absorbing what I knew, I decided to go inside my home for a bit and lie down. My thinking was, no matter what, this could be a long day emotionally, mentally and physically, and I needed to do my best to prepare for whatever was ahead for Peter.

I didn't lie down for long, maybe ten to fifteen minutes. Fortunately, we live in an area where the hospital is a ten- or fifteen-minute drive from our house. Lying down and gathering my thoughts refocused me and I felt okay to drive on my own. I grabbed a book, water, and some snack bars, expecting to be at the hospital for a while.

When I found Peter in the hospital's emergency room, he was sitting up on a gurney, and his left hand was bandaged. When he saw me he said the first thing that entered his head when the accident happened was, "Chris is going to kill me." We shared a quick giggle, and then Peter's expression got more serious and he said soberly, "It's really bad." I said, "You're in an amazing hospital," and he replied, "No it's really bad." Shortly thereafter, several doctors gathered to discuss his surgery and have us sign the release paperwork. They started going on about what they were trying to save, and I stopped them and asked what we were dealing with. They asked me, "Oh, you didn't see it?" and I said, "No, I don't need to see it, but can you tell me about his hand?"

They explained that his middle and ring fingers were partially attached and he had lost parts of his index finger and thumb. The pinky was the only fully intact finger. They weren't sure what could be saved or reattached, but they'd do their best to save as much as possible. I said I would stick around, and the lead doctor, with a perplexed look on his face, asked, "Do you live far from here?" I replied no, I only lived ten or fifteen minutes away. He strongly encouraged me to go home, adding that the surgery could take anywhere from five to ten hours. Peter and I discussed it, made a list of people for me to call, and mutually agreed that I would go home while he was in surgery.

Ironically, I was in the middle of taking an eight-week Mindfulness-Based Stress Reduction (MBSR) class, and the fourth week's class was meeting that night. When I got home, after making the necessary calls to family and work, I called my instructor. The call went to her voicemail, and I let her know my husband needed unexpected surgery, I wasn't sure when he would get out, and I didn't want to disrupt the class if I were to get a phone call in the middle of class and/or needed to leave mid-class. She called back within an hour and said one word, "Come." I did, and I ended up getting a call from Peter's surgeon near the end of the class, explaining what they were able to do and not do. (They reattached the thumb, but Peter would lose all of the ring and middle fingers, and half of the index finger.) Peter was in recovery and would be in his hospital room in about an hour or two. It all worked out for me to stay for the entire class that night and go to the hospital immediately afterward.

That began a journey of Peter ultimately losing the part of his thumb that had been reattached, and the hospital misplacing and then finding his (stretched-out) wedding ring. There was uncertainty about whether and when he would be able to resume his job, or what type of work he'd be able to do. At the time, he worked as a dining services director for an assisted living community, so he cooked daily. There was also uncertainty about how much use he would have from what remained of his hand. When he start-ed occupational therapy less than a week after his accident, the therapist removed the surgical dressing to examine his hand. She looked each of us straight in the eyes with the utmost confidence and stated, "You will get a lot of use out of this hand."

Looking back, I had all kinds of thoughts running through my head. Be-sides the practical matters listed above, how would Peter mentally respond to what happened to him? Would he get into a funk or a depression? What would he need for support overall during this process, and from me, his wife and life partner, and what would that look like? I felt that continuing to attend the MBSR class was the perfect serendipity for me, and I learned five key lessons in presence from that experience:

1. **Going toward pain, instead of moving away from or ignoring it, helps in dealing with the pain.** There were several examples of dealing with emotional pain in the early weeks following the accident: looking at his hand when they changed the dressing, listening intently to sur-geons when they explained the risk factors with his surgery, allowing myself to cry when I learned they could not save his thumb. Flowing with the waves of pain, while uncomfortable at the time, does help us move through it. It can help soften our associated emotions and give us clarity about how to respond. If we ignore or deny those feel-ings, the pain's sting persists, making it challenging to see a way out.

2. **Keep two feet planted firmly on the ground and sit with a dignified posture to stay grounded.** I mean this literally. Instead of crossing my legs when seated, putting both feet flat on the ground when someone was explaining something or while I observed an occupational thera-py session helped me to connect and focus on what was in front of me. Even now, one way I reconnect to this present moment, whether stand-ing or sitting, is being aware of my feet in my shoes or on the ground.

3. **Thoughts can keep me from my experience.** My experience is what is happening right now. Not thinking about the past, putting a judgment or label on what is now happening, or worrying about what might or might not happen in the future. This is a biggie, recognizing thoughts

are just concepts that pop up in your head – not reality. You are not your thoughts: the brain is separate from who you are. Being here and alive is what connects us to others. It keeps us plugged into life's energy.

4. **Your breath is an anchor.** When you get caught up in a thought, or wrapped up in a reaction, refocus on your in breath and out breath to re-anchor yourself to the present. The present is where your power lies. There were countless "what if's" in the aftermath of my husband's accident, but I ultimately got to a point where I chuckled or smiled when they came up. Some led to actions to take: a question for Peter's human resources rep, a point to make to his occupational therapist. It's then a conscious choice to let it go and refocus on breathing in and out.

5. **Every breath is a new beginning, inhaling new life, exhaling old stuff, an opportunity for a new start.** This is major. Pete's accident forced him into multiple new beginnings. While progress was incremental, it moved in the right direction. The left hand he now had was new to him and his body, and it took a while for his brain to catch up to what is currently there and how to use it optimally. As with habit change, it can take a while for the brain to catch up in integrating and routinely using a new habit. Repetition, while in presence, helps to instill adjustments to doing and being.

Taking on a new perspective comes into play here, too. We both realized Pete could have bled to death if our next-door neighbor hadn't heard his calls for help and run over with a tourniquet. We'll take him alive with fewer fingers, versus not being here at all.

Even though I'm using an accident to illustrate these tenets, you don't need to wait for an accident to put these presence concepts into place. You can start to change your life in a second by applying these principles. You can cultivate awareness to make a new choice in how you respond to life's events. I will add that maintaining a 45-minute-a-day home mindfulness practice (the homework during my eight-week MBSR class) directly contributed to my cultivating this level of awareness and inner peace during the aftermath of my husband's accident.

Applying the presence triad in this experience, the principles of inten-tion, purposeful attention (mindfulness), and impulse control came up re-peatedly, and at different levels of granularity. For example, the intention for Peter to get some level of functionality back in his hand was his top focus for the four months he was out of work. My **intention** in supporting him was following his lead: whatever he needed on a particular day, from a ride, or refilling his prescription or coordinating visitors, to dealing with all the decisions around work and short-term disability, and simply just being there in the moment. I have to say, he was a superstar patient: he never went down the "why me" route, did all the occupational therapy "homework exercises" and initiated and delved into the research for getting a prosthetic.

Purposeful attention meant maintaining a meditation practice that helped to instill the ability for me to be present to all that was happening and to stop myself going down the paths of "what if he can't cook again" or "what if he can't work again." Staying present with that day, that hour, that mo-ment, as needed, was a real-life way to put everything I learned in the MBSR course and before into practice. This worked similarly for **impulse control**. At one point I wondered if I would need to take on more work to make up for income lost due to Peter's absence from work. Again, rather than jumping to conclusions before things were sorted out, I brought myself back to the present to recognize that this was not a decision I needed to make quite yet. You'll find that being present has a wonderful, sometimes seemingly mag-ical ripple effect. Presence enables you to loosen the grip of mind chatter and ego-initiated stories like those you identified in Chapter 1. You're more proactive and seldom reactive. You're less likely to operate on autopilot. You take more interest in what is being said versus your own standpoint. As you build the muscle of presence-driven focus, you'll see nuances in people and situations that you previously missed. Your intuition will be resurrected and you'll be better positioned to hear its guidance more often. People may ex-perience you differently, and may not be able to pinpoint why.

Intentionally Soothe

With presence-driven focus, you also gain the ability to intentionally soothe yourself. Mindless or emotional eating comes up as a common challenge with my clients; you can view this as a way of attempting to soothe that backfires energetically. This action typically arises from being stressed or bored, a habit when watching TV or after dinner, "eating" uncomfortable feelings, or coming from the "clean your plate" mentality instilled in many of us as children. Eating mindlessly or emotionally in this way not only impacts your weight, but also affects your focus, concentration and energy. There are ways that you can intentionally soothe as both a method of renewing your energy and being present. Note that most of these examples do not involve food:

- **Listen to music** (really paying attention to the instruments, lyrics, and voices).
- **Enjoy a cup of coffee or tea** (savor the flavor; appreciate the temperature).
- **Walk mindfully** (minus a cell phone, texting, talking or music). Notice your pace, how your feet feel touching the ground, in your shoes. Observe your posture. Take in your surroundings.
- **Express gratitude.** Write down three to five things that you are grateful for, today.
- **Breathe mindfully.** Notice your breath, watch and feel it flow through your nostrils and/or mouth. Observe any outside thoughts that occur, and let them float off like clouds that go by. Return to the breath.
- **Consciously limit over-consumption.** Instead of the entire bag of chips, have the listed serving size. Instead of a bottle of wine, drink one five-ounce glass. To take it to the next level of wellness, try a healthy, yet tasteful substitution. The crunch of nuts, apples or pickles instead of chips. Sparkling flavored or fruit-infused water instead of wine or soda. Eat slowly, tasting each bite, sensing the food's smell and texture. Instead of an entire night of channel surfing or binge-watching, choose specific programs that entertain or educate. Whatever you select, watch fully. Avoid multitasking.
- **Read purposefully.** Choose books and magazines for entertainment, education, information, nourishment or growth. For internet reading, to avoid getting engrossed in one website after another (the online counterpart of TV channel-surfing), decide in advance how much time you will spend reading online and stick to it.

- **Pray.** Use a spiritual or religious text and verses that speak to you. Make up your own prayer for what you want to communicate to your Source.
- **Build, create or grow something.** Woodworking, needlework, drawing, painting, writing, gardening, glassblowing, throwing pottery and mentoring fall into this arena.

A Note on the Perils of Multitasking

I would be remiss in discussing presence without addressing multitasking. I know many women feel they have perfected multitasking. If we're talking about having multiple projects on your plate at once, delegating tasks to others, or even running several machines in the background at once, like starting the washer, dryer, and dishwasher, and then prepping dinner, sure, I'm all for efficiency with how we manage people, tools and resources that make us more productive. It's the "switchtasking," a term used by Dave Crenshaw in his book *The Myth of Multitasking*, that I discourage. Crenshaw defines switchtasking as attempting to do multiple attention-requiring tasks at the same time. We all know about distracted driving and the horrific implications of that behavior. How about limiting *distracted living*? I'll address setting boundaries later in Chapter 9, which is one strategy to help on this front.

While life is unpredictable, we can control how we approach it, and have a method to respond to the potential interruptions that can hijack our attention and disrupt our energy. I'm talking about things like phones buzzing and ringing; email and instant message notifications on our computers; checking email, social media and the internet at frequent intervals while you have another task or person in front of (or on the phone with) you. Funny coincidence, as I took a break from writing this chapter, one of my colleagues posted on Facebook: "When opportunity knocks, open the door. It's when we're too busy to see what's in front of us – we miss it." While that statement could be taken several different ways, my perspective is that when we're not present, we miss all kinds of hidden gems and opportunities. We miss *life* – from ways to be innovative and problem-solve or develop more intimate and authentic relationships, to improved communication and well-being and experiencing deep joy and rewards.

Ultimately, monotasking (instead of multitasking) opens the door to create a life of rich ways to be of service in doing what is important to us, sharing our strengths and our light. As Eckhart Tolle says, "There is great depth in doing one thing at a time. Don't treat a moment, activity or task as a stepping stone (when you do that, it reduces the aliveness of the moment). Peace then flows into what you do. Avoid reducing each moment as a means to an end. Enjoy the journey. It's all about the journey."

At this point, you've digested a number of presence-related stories, tips and lessons in this chapter. How do you translate all these stories and concepts into presence-driven focus for yourself? First, consider that it is a *practice*: don't strive to be present 100% of the time. Look instead to amp up your presence.

To use a metaphor from Jeri's yoga class story earlier, focus on *your* presence "mat." There are two ways you can begin to approach that, and I advise having both in your life:

1. instituting a meditation and/or journaling practice (examples of doing), and
2. infusing presence principles in how you show up (ways of being)

EXERCISE ONE: START A MEDITATIVE PRACTICE

OPTION 1: MEDITATION. If you aren't yet meditating, one way to begin is practicing mindful meditation, in which you sit and be with your in and out breath.

1. First, as was taught to me in my MBSR class, take a dignified seat. Sit in a chair, placing both feet flat on the ground.
2. Now focus on the base of your spine and use that area to support the rest of your back.
3. Relax your shoulders, head straight. You can either close your eyes or glance down toward the ground.
4. Notice how your body is feeling, and the sensations of your feet on the ground, thighs and buttocks against the chair, hands where they are resting.
5. For your breathing, pay attention to your inhale and exhale. You're not trying to control your breath in any way. Just notice. Observe

the breath in and out of your nostrils, in and out of your mouth. Be aware of the parts of your body expanding and contracting with each breath. Think of it as your body breathing you, versus you breathing your body.

6. As you conduct this mindful meditation, other sensations might occur for you, such as thoughts in your head, feelings in your body, various emotions popping up. That's fine, and normal. When that happens, simply acknowledge it, and then gently escort your attention back to watching your breath. If you need a visual, consider an image of a feather skimming the edge of a glass: that's the level of gentleness to emulate. The idea is to build your muscle of attention, which you apply at future times where you sit and meditate or in everyday activities.

Meditation is free, and readily accessible: you're breathing anyway! I will sometimes get pushback from clients that they don't have enough time to meditate. If you're struggling with figuring out how to fit it in, you don't need to start with thirty or more minutes: start with five and build up from there. Tie it to another routine, and insert it before or after. Or, working with the notion of presence, think about the habits in your life that detract from your ability to be present, or times where you're zoning out with the TV, movies, phone or social media. What might it be like to reduce or eliminate those habits and substitute mindful meditation instead? Treat this as an experiment – play with it, release any expectations, and see what you experience.

OPTION 2: JOURNALING. As a practice, journaling is another way to check in, ground and center yourself. I particularly like Julia Cameron's "morning pages" exercise described in her book, *The Artist's Way*. Basically, treat a journal-writing session like a brain dump: write whatever comes out of your head onto the page, filling up three pages. Let go of grammar, spelling, how your penmanship looks, whether any of it connects or makes sense. This exercise is simply intended to release the thoughts in your head. These pages are not something you'll show someone else, and the goal isn't beautiful prose. It's intended to help you give voice to the mind, and ultimately bring you clarity. When you do this in the morning, a side benefit is clearing the cobwebs for the day. The key is to *write on paper*, not type on a keyboard. Use a notebook, legal pad or journal and pen.

EXERCISE TWO: WEAVE PRESENCE PRINCIPLES INTO YOUR LIFE

This exercise addresses infusing presence principles as a life practice. Be creative here. Make a sport of it. You can incorporate these principles around something strategic like life, career, business or health decisions, or play a game with yourself and seek ways to be present as you go through your day. For example, when you walk, do so *mindfully* – don't look down and text or talk on the phone. Notice your pace and posture, the smells, sights and sounds around you, and how your feet feel as they touch the ground. Try being present when you're commuting to work, or having conversations one-on-one, in meetings, or over the phone. Be present in how you respond to emails, texts, and calls.

- **TO OBSERVE OR SET**: What is your **intention** for each encounter? What do you notice happening for you at certain parts of the day, or in particular situations?

- **TO ESTABLISH**: How do you create an environment that gives you the **focus** necessary for what's currently in front of you?

- **TO RESET/REGROUP**: When you feel your **attention** waning or your habitual **impulsive** action about to jump in or create a story about what's happening, how do you press pause and catch yourself? What helps you to reset your attention and/or choose a less destructive response to a triggering event? When do you need a time-out, and what helps you regroup or see a situation with fresh eyes?

Don't limit these inquiries to the workplace; apply them outside the work setting as well.

- When you're commuting and either stopped in traffic or at a stop light or sign, notice your breath, posture, weather, the objects and scenery outside your vehicle.

- When your work day is complete, how do you transition from work mode to being present for non-work mode? Do you change your clothes, play some music, walk or do other physical movement?
- If you live with others, how do you greet them when you get home? Do you need space or decompression time to be optimally present with them?
- On the weekday or weekends – household chores, hobbies, errands, eating, physical activity, socializing – all are ripe for presence-driven focus.
  - See how long you can avoid looking at your phone. Take it a step further and try shutting off notifications (or shutting off the phone completely).
  - Beware of excess "zone-out" time in front of the TV, video games, or smartphone, and set limits on the time you spend with these devices.
- When you are engaged in an activity, simply be in that place fully: wash the dishes, garden, eat your meal at a dining table, watch your child's sporting event or performance.
- Wake up your senses: notice the sounds, colors, smells, textures. What's it like to absorb yourself in the task in front of you? In truth, your current task is the only reality: the past is gone and the future is unknown. Why not make the most of that current task? *Engage.*

As part of this exercise, you might choose one work-related circumstance and one scenario outside of work in which to apply these principles, for the next two weeks. Again, bring a mindset of curiosity, purely to see what your experience is. Document your observations.

Thus far in this chapter, we've focused on internal presence: various actions and ways of being to be present within. As you build the capacity for being internally present, use that as a springboard to create the presence that you impart to the world, as addressed in this next exercise.

EXERCISE THREE: BRING AWARENESS TO THE VIBE
YOU'RE BROADCASTING

Decide how you want to show up in the world, overall and in specific situations. Journal on the following questions:

- What is the energy you want to bring to what's in front of you?
- What do you want to demonstrate by your tone, appearance, level of attention and interest, posture/body language?
- Where is there a place for displaying traits like compassion, receptivity, boldness, courage, vulnerability, acceptance and patience? (Note that having these qualities for yourself enables you to show them to the outside world.)

Here's another way to look at this, and another avenue for further self-inquiry: consider the signals you're transmitting with your type of energy and level of presence.

- What messages are you sending in the way you present yourself and your values, in terms of the energy and level of presence you're broadcasting? For those of you who have your own business or who are in sales, you are literally the face or brand of your business. For others, think of how your presence aligns with the identity you want to foster.
- Revisit the energized story you wrote in Chapter 1. How does your current state of presence reflect that story? What is the gap between your external presence and the story you want to live into?
- What do you want more of in your energy and health, and how well is that aligned with where you're predominantly directing your attention and focus?
- If you feel too close to this and can't accurately discern how others perceive you, get input from some trusted friends. How would they describe the qualities radiating from you when they are in your presence? If you work for someone else, when was the last time you had a conversation with your manager about your presence at work? If other people report to you or you consistently work with several

peers, get their input. What do they appreciate about how you show up, and what opportunities for improvement do they see, that they feel will help you improve your performance? You could even conduct a 360° assessment, in order to get anonymous feedback from multiple sources.

~~~~~~~~~~~~~~

Consciously choosing to be alert and attentive internally and externally provides a clear channel to be the blessing discussed in Chapter 5, to live with self-love and compassion. The new story you wrote in Chapter 1, blended with love, compassion and presence principles, gives you the mindset and awareness to see your current state of energy and what will best support you (and what you can let go of) in enabling burnout-proof living. When you are grounded internally, and come from a place of self-love and self-honor, that maximizes your ability to be balanced externally. Again, revisit your new energizing story and your Wellness Vision, in finalizing your selection of presence exercises to perform in this chapter.

CHAPTER SEVEN

Play in Energized Places

"To be fully engaged, we must be physically energized, emotionally connected, mentally focused and spiritually aligned with a purpose beyond our immediate self-interest."

~JIM LOEHR

Energy and presence are tied closely together. When people think of igniting their energy, most immediately jump to the idea of high-voltage energy. My goal in this chapter is to create awareness around the different types of energy available to you, so you can choose from among the buffet of options what will best suit your particular needs in burnout-proofing your well-being. The opposite of burnout is the ability to be steadily engaged with positive, consistent energy.

Back in Chapter 2, you identified energy infusers and energy drains in the Energy Evaluation. That review scratched the surface on the topic of energy. To take that discussion deeper, let's think now about different buckets of energy:

- Physical
- Emotional
- Mental, and
- Spiritual.

I first encountered energy partitioned this way in reading *The Power of Full Engagement* by Jim Loehr and Tony Schwartz, likely around the time their book was published in 2003. In fact, for me, their book was a seminal read that impacted three main phases of my life:

- First, the book influenced how I approached my level of engagement in the first years of my life as an entrepreneur.

- Second, a few years later when I was diagnosed with MS, after I initially caught my breath, the book's ideas helped me choose the types of energy to create for myself.
- Third, after I launched Priority Wellness, the book's ideas influenced my choice to shift into energy management as a core focus of my business.

Let's summarize these buckets of energy:

- **PHYSICAL ENERGY is** *health*. This is most folks' initial default when they hear the word "energy" in the context of health and wellness. How are you routinely renewing/recharging?
- **EMOTIONAL ENERGY is** *happiness*. What helps you cultivate and display an optimistic mindset of opportunity, enjoyment and adventure?
- **MENTAL ENERGY is the ability to** *focus* in an engrossed way on the most important tasks or situations and define when and where you carve out space for making progress on essential projects.
- **SPIRITUAL ENERGY is a sense of** *purpose*: doing more of what you do best and enjoy most in feeling connected and congruent with your big whys. Being stirred by something larger than yourself, as in a higher purpose, power or cause.

What does awareness of these different types of energy give you? I see it as engaging and adjusting different lenses for what's working well for you in each of these areas and where the opportunities for improvement lie. Look at this as the equivalent of running on all four cylinders: your life and energy will optimally hum when you're consistently addressing each of these pieces. If the concept of increasing your energy feels too big, this is a way to start breaking it down into manageable chunks.

The Energy vs. Time Debate

Part of my business includes speaking at networking events, professional organizations, companies and conferences. I will periodically get asked to speak on time management. My typical response is, "While I can do that, I recommend instead that I speak on energy management, as your audience will benefit more from that talk." You see, time is finite. We all have the same twenty-four hours a day and seven days a week to get everything done and live our lives. Our IQ, socioeconomic status, gender, and age don't change the number of minutes available in a day. You can't add or subtract minutes via time management. Sure, you can be more efficient with your time, and while I advocate doing so (and weave some tips on this into the next chapter that dovetail well with energy management), you'll ultimately hit a wall.

The common mistaken philosophy I hear from people: "Oh, I just need to work harder." Or wishing "If only I had more time." I disagree, as pushing through or hoping for time to open up without examining your energizing habits dismisses how you feel, your brain capacity, your emotions, and your level of focus and alertness. When you look instead at what gives you energy and what drains your energy, your natural energy highs and lows throughout the day, along with the different types of energy to leverage, it opens things up in a new way. Once you master how you manage your various energies, it's like time magically expands. Consciously choosing and fueling yourself in the type of energies that will best help you create and live the reality of your Wellness Vision is a powerful tactic to ward off burnout.

I don't necessarily mean you need to be the Energizer Bunny 100% of the time: my intention in this chapter is to help you develop some energy awareness and then explore energy intelligence in Chapter 8, so you can select what to make a part of your life. It's also not about being happy all the time. It's about deliberately using your energy in the best possible way to consistently fuel you.

For example, Gertrude has found that a practice of detachment has helped her in multiple ways, including healing more quickly from family deaths, including aunts and uncles, her sister, and grandniece (the latter two under separate unexpected circumstances). Eastern philosophies have always resonated for her, and over the years, she has been exposed to various techniques, including Reiki, and a healing school where she spent two years learning to be a shaman. She recharges via quiet time, and has happily lived by herself for many years. In her twenties, Gertrude noticed how frequently she was getting sick, which was the impetus for her to step back and reassess how she could enable herself to be healthier more often. Now in her fifties and reflecting on past decades, she shifted her perception of activities like volunteering from being an obligation to a choice. Making the wording shift to "choose to" instead of "have to" lifted her energy and helped her see what to keep and release.

Today, Gertrude is frequently told that a calming light emanates from her and that she is a presence that helps others calm down. She makes space for thinking and pondering, doing practices appropriate for each situation. She routinely presses pause, contemplates and asks, "What do I need?" Practical actions might look like lying down in silence, reading, research, sitting, or envisioning. She has green tea daily, and enjoys being with her cats and checking in with herself. The language she uses to function under is "being peace." This intentional mantra has become a part of her being as she moves through the world. Gertrude tends to look more at the bigger picture – taking a worldwide view. She's reminded at different points in life that there are bigger things to learn, and she has an awareness of consequences.

Gertrude has always had and created artwork in her life, understanding that producing art serves as a meditation for her. She describes her most recent inspiration as follows: "I have been integrating one of Thich Nhat Hanh's messages, which I have as one of his beautiful calligraphy paintings: 'peace in oneself, peace in the world.' I first learned of him when I was drawn to and purchased a used copy of his book *Being Peace*. I remember thinking that those words, 'being peace,' encompassed the meaning of life, the essence of everything to me."

Gertrude adds: "I find that as time goes on, and I live increasingly aligned to my values, I feel a greater sense of peace and joy. One of the greatest leaps in living my authentic self was when I became vegetarian and later, vegan. I feel that burdens are lifted when I make changes that support my beliefs, such as leaving taiko (Japanese drumming) because I do not want to play on animal skins. While some may equate energy and vitality with being physically active, I see that energy and vitality can have different meanings to everyone. For example, for me it manifests in being peace. Service to others can also bring me energy and vitality. When I advocate and volunteer for animals, the environment or human rights, I feel energized in a sense of purpose. And, my energy and vitality can help me to be in service to others."

Let's review Gertrude's story to see how the different energy aspects show up for a particular individual and how they integrate with each other. To address her physical energy, she found that quiet contemplative practices help her be more resilient. These ways of "being" aligned with and clarified her overall purpose, which drives the types of volunteering and hobbies she's involved with and even the food she consumes: fueling a combination of spiritual and physical energy. The level of calming presence she's created, along with her strong sense of purpose, feeds into her focus and optimism: addressing a blend of mental and emotional energy.

Kay considers herself spiritual but not religious, taking a lot from nature, which she happens to be surrounded by at her home in rural Ohio. The quietness of the lakes and paths in the woods has been healing and powerful to her. She finds this outdoor sanctuary helps her to get outside of herself and unplug, and it insulates her like a big virtual hug. During her walks, she might see a bug or plant she hadn't noticed before; it reminds her that something bigger exists, which she appreciates and respects. For her physical care, she enjoys cooking and eats well, loves yoga and gets massages. She paints nearly daily in oils. Kay feels that the ability for her to be a teacher for her daughter's caregiver, Mandy, has been a gift. Mandy's been able to help Kay assist her adult daughter, Brittany, who has intractable epilepsy as well as mental health and behavior challenges. Together, Kay and Mandy work almost daily on Brittany's behalf, along with facing the medical community and doctors. Despite these circumstances, Kay remains, as she says, "mostly positive." Kay continues: "I don't feel like a victim: what helps me stay positive is the historical value of what I've persevered through. I have a lot of wisdom about positive things, and have the power and strength to make each day better. Frequent mantras I'll recite are 'today's going to be better. I'm going to be better.' I always try to do my very best. If I don't know what to do, I'll find out or ask."

Deb, a fifty-year-old self-employed executive and leadership coach, has found that she doesn't force her energy as much as she used to. Instead, she trusts it. That might mean tackling only two things on a long to-do list. She doesn't like working at night, but sometimes, roughly every six to eight weeks, inspiration hits and she'll follow it. The energy will come out when it's ready, and at that point, she rides it. She feels fortunate to have created a life and situation that allow her to do that, including not scheduling meetings before 10:30 a.m. most weeks. When she finds herself pressing for energy at times when there's none to be had, she'll take a break instead of plowing through. Such a break might include watching the latest episode in the current TV drama she's following. If something has to get done today, that may be the case, but it might not need to be done *this very minute*: that line of thinking has been hugely liberating for her. Reflecting on this, Deb says, "This approach helps to take the focus off 'little me' and what's going on in my office. It energetically shifts the lens to how I'm viewing the world. When I let go of my tightly held perspective of what's in front of me, it allows me to come back bigger."

Each of the above personal stories illustrates the variety of ways these professional women have advanced their physical, mental, emotional and/or spiritual energy. I hope reading about their methods has begun to spark your own ideas about potential methods you can experiment with now.

Let's approach each of these "energy buckets" in further depth. Note that each plays a role in your effectiveness in fostering burnout-proof living – dancing and deliberately moving and partnering with life's energy, instead of simply existing.

Physical Energy

Generating physical energy doesn't necessarily mean you have to join a gym. This is a frequent misconception I hear from clients when they start working with me.

While going to the gym may appeal to some folks, that setting doesn't work for everyone. Consider the variety of ways you can integrate movement into your life without joining a gym:

- Try "deskercise" and other options at work – yoga-type stretching or strengthening movements in your desk area, ranging from wall or desk push-ups to squats or stretches that you can do with an arm band. A resistance kit of stretch bands and straps can give you a full-body workout at home or while traveling. Any place you have stairs or access to bleachers offers potential for climbing up and down. Also look for safe sidewalks, tracks, bike paths, walking paths and trails, along with shopping malls that open early for mall walkers.

- Geocaching. This practice is like an adult scavenger or treasure hunt, using an app. You can search for geocaching sites in your area and see where they take you. It's a unique way to integrate some fun with outdoor movement.
- Metal detecting – get to a local beach, walk for hours in the sand, and pick up some "treasures" along the way.
- Take a class in something that moves and/or physically stretches and strengthens you, like belly dancing, boxing, rock or rope climbing, hula hooping, aerial yoga swing, Essentrics, or martial arts.
- If you like exercising with a group, look into classes including yoga, barre, cycling, and CrossFit. Investigate joining a sporting league for bowling, golf, volleyball, soccer, baseball, or softball.
- Get wet! Swim in a pool, local pond, lake or ocean. Try out a canoe, kayak, or paddleboard, or take water aerobics classes.
- Get physical with chores. Chop wood, move large heavy objects in a wheelbarrow from one place to another.
- Have a personal trainer come to your home and setup a routine for you.

Let's not forget the "renew and recharge" aspect of physical energy. While movement may help some people become physically refreshed, others may need downtime, in the form of quality and/or quantity sleep overnight, an afternoon nap, or sitting in silence or meditation.

While we're on the topic of physical energy, pay attention to your posture, and use proper posture when sitting and standing. Doing so helps your muscles to work more efficiently, resulting in your body using less energy. If you spend a lot of time driving, be sure to also check on your posture periodically, in traffic or at red lights, for example. The American Chiropractic Association offers helpful posture tips.[1]

Emotional Energy

If you think in terms of movement, what can keep us stuck, emotionally, is having a fixed mindset toward a set of circumstances. Inflicting a hefty

1 www.acatoday.org/content/posture-power-how-to-correct-your-body-alignment.

dose of judgment and/or criticism (whether self-directed or aimed at others) about a situation. Stifling our emotions, or numbing them with food, TV/Netflix, mindless web-surfing or app use, work, or other activities. Behaving in this manner doesn't allow room to change and is an energy drain.

You can instead approach circumstances from different angles to create positive emotional energy. Play with a growth mindset – what is there to learn from a particular situation? What is this phase, episode, or circumstance asking from me, in terms of my development? How can I treat this occurrence like an adventure? What positive elements can I see? In what ways can I give myself (or someone else) the benefit of the doubt?

You don't need to wait for a specific event to occur to decide to be happy. So often I'll hear, "I'll be happy when/after …"

- I get a certain job
- I'm at my dream weight or clothing size
- better weather arrives
- I can take a vacation
- the kids are out of school/out on their own
- I retire.

While you're reading this book (and afterwards), please don't postpone happiness or any other type of emotional satisfaction until you attain your Wellness Vision. Choose to be happy now! Fill your emotional energy bucket with what brings you joy. It can be simple things, like listening to a song, having a conversation with a friend, playing with a pet, sitting in nature, acknowledging the people and aspects of life for which you are grateful, or identifying what's good now.

EXERCISE ONE: PLAY WITH EMOTIONAL ENERGY
Review your Wellness Vision and imagine the emotions you will experience upon attaining that vision. What emotions did you notice? Where did they show up in your body? How can you regularly instill these emotions as you progress toward your Wellness Vision? Select methods to create those emotions now and observe the impact of these emotions on your journey. Dance with the growth and curious mindset by periodically reviewing your Wellness

Vision and asking yourself the questions posed in the second paragraph of this Emotional Energy section.

Mental Energy

If you want to strengthen your focus and haven't already read Chapter 4 and Chapter 6, start there. Both chapters provide you with the foundational support for building mental space and capacity. Here are five ways to supplement your mental energy:

1. Practice masterful task-blocking,
2. Leverage your natural rhythms,
3. Prioritize daily activities,
4. Establish quality/quantity sleep, and
5. Maximize nutrition.

Let's take a closer look at each one.

1. PRACTICE MASTERFUL TASK-BLOCKING

Masterful task-blocking is identifying the most important activities on your schedule, blocking out the time for those activities (in 90-minute chunks, based on research performed by psychophysiologist Peretz Lavie, on what he called "ultradian rhythms": our natural energy cycles during the day), and removing or minimizing distractions during those scheduled blocks of time. For example, while writing this book, on my best writing days, I built in at least one 90-minute block. During those ninety minutes, I didn't read or send email, receive or make calls or check my phone for texts. (In fact, I shut off my phone's text/email notifications years ago as an experiment, and I've never found the need to turn them back on again.) I only opened my web browser if I needed to look up something relevant to what I was writing and then I shut down my browser again. Other than my browser and Word, when I was in my writing block, I had no other windows open on my laptop. Because this book was the top priority on my writing days, I also scheduled this writing block to be done first, after I completed my morning routine. This routine is currently journaling, breakfast, meditation and prayer, and only then checking for messages I'm expecting. Rather than being interrupted by emails and calls, I set up other time blocks in the day for reading/responding to emails and making/returning calls. Because I find I'm more productive when I write in the morning, I avoided scheduling meetings any time before 11 a.m.

You can use task blocks for professional and personal projects, "me time" and other health-related activities or appointments, administrative tasks, and social connections. You can also use them for matters that you have deemed important and are related to your Wellness Vision.

Creating task blocks, blended with intentional energy management, is a highly effective way to improve your performance. You could even block out 15- to 30-minute open chunks here and there as "breathing gaps" to use between appointments, or if a task or appointment runs over the estimated time, or if an unforeseen urgent issue arises. In the places where you have control of your schedule, maximize task blocks. This may be easier for those of you who have your own business, but even for those who work for someone else, in the parts of the day where you manage your own time, I advocate task-blocking.

2. LEVERAGE YOUR NATURAL RHYTHMS

Here are some other ways to effectively use your daily mental energy. Related to one of the points Deb made in her story earlier in this chapter, use your natural energy highs and lows to your advantage. If you don't have a sense of when you feel most mentally and physically "on," track and log your energy for a week. Every hour or so, check in with how you felt – at least physically and mentally – during that time, and rate your performance on the tasks you completed in that time period. When you feel like you have a good sense of your energy ebbs and flows, arrange your work, when possible, to match those cycles. Plan highly cerebral, focused work for when you have your greatest mental energy. Return texts, emails and phone calls and perform other administrative work during lower-energy times. Inject a mental or physical energy boost as needed prior to a block of focused time to feed that block. Notice how when and what you eat or drink impacts your physical, mental and even emotional energy. (You could even perform Chapter 8's *Exercise One, Observe Food and Beverage Impact.*)

3. PRIORITIZE DAILY ACTIVITIES

Prioritizing your daily activities can also give you more control and momentum in the mental energy of your day. Either the night before or first thing in the morning, write down the two to three most important tasks that are most essential for you to complete today. If your job involves a lot of paper, what can help get this done, is an old-fashioned banker's box (or a file drawer) and hanging file folders. In fact, one of my clients, Kara, is a vice president of a bank who used this method to help her regain control of her day. Create folders for every day of the month, numbered 1 through 31, and a folder for each month, labeled January through December. Keep the folders for days at the front of the box, folders for months at the back. File the paperwork relevant to a particular day in the appropriate folder. The current day's file is at the front of the banker's box. You start by filing papers as memory triggers or for future actions to take on the appropriate day of the current month or in a future month.

As you start your day, open the day's file, and prioritize the papers/projects to address that day: some may already be done, some can be delegated, and some can be postponed to another day. When you've prioritized today's projects, block them on your calendar and get to work. When you've emptied out today's folder, move it to the back of the numbered folders. The monthly folders are behind the numbered folders, with next month first. When you get to the end of the month, open up the next month's folder, and file the papers in the appropriate days of the month, and start the process all over again. You can use this tool in your work setting (as Kara does), at home for paying bills, or to trigger your memory for future RSVPs or other actions to take.

4 & 5. ESTABLISH QUALITY/QUANTITY SLEEP AND MAXIMIZE NUTRITION

Plenty of quality sleep and good nutrition (maximizing your intake of nutrient-dense foods) not only impact mental energy, but also your physical and even emotional energy. Think about how your focus and thinking are affected, how irritable you can get, and your lack of get-up-and-go if you had a bad night's sleep, haven't eaten in a while, or consume nutrient-poor foods. Given that these qualities impact multiple energy buckets and areas of your life, we'll look more closely at these aspects in Chapter 8.

Spiritual Energy

What matters most to you? What feeds you at the deepest level? What connects and reconnects you to what's most important?

What reminds you of something larger than yourself? Is it being in nature? Participating in a service in a house of worship or being part of some form of fellowship? Prayer? Silence? Being part of a charitable organization, fundraiser or social justice cause? Being inspired by the achievements of other human beings, on whatever scale?

What are you here to contribute? While you are living, what are you creating to leave behind? That could take the form of relationships you built, items you produced, people you influenced, talents you shared, situations you improved, problems you solved, and/or individuals or other living things you loved.

Having a sense of our big-picture role here (beyond our job title or other roles we may use to identify and label ourselves) and tapping into ways beyond the intellectual to habitually inspire us ultimately fuel our humanity. It's leveraging the totality of what's accessible to us – mind, body, and spirit. What can burn us out is relying too heavily on the mind/ego aspect to do things and/or figure things out, and forgetting or neglecting the emotional, mental and physical messages from the body and/or the bottomless resources available from the spiritual realm.

Inspiring energy can be viewed as a type of spiritual energy ("inspired" meaning "in spirit"). You can think of it as planting and fertilizing seeds in this energy bucket – that may also help you further clarify what matters to you. You'll find this energy in recognizing situations that illustrate hope, boldness, bravery, optimism, overcoming the odds, and/or tapping into spiritual resources. When we see what other human beings achieve, and what drives and propels them, it's a reminder that what's possible for them is accessible and available to us.

What gives you an inspirational jolt? What lessons from others can you adapt and mold into your own life? You may find such lessons in a TED talk or motivational speech, sports competitions, art, architecture, a podcast, a memoir, a novel, a film, or spiritual texts. What puts you in inspirational space? Meditation? Prayer? Silence? Nature? It doesn't have to be something extreme like climbing Mount Everest. It could be as simple as observing toddlers at play – creating their own entertainment, using their imagination, displaying their innate curiosity. It reminds you of the capacities and talents within that your life situations may have temporarily suppressed.

Start with the perspective of the extraordinary illustrated in everyday occurrences. Expect, watch for, and acknowledge miracles daily. The fact that you're continually breathing, with blood pumping through your veins and your heart beating, is a miracle. The sun rises and sets daily as the earth continually rotates on its axis in space. There is something beyond you that makes that happen.

There may be certain beings (God or gods, goddesses, guides, spirits and/ or angels) that resonate with you. You might use a variety of ways to connect with such forms of existence, whether through prayer, meditation, journaling, or oracle cards. I personally own several oracle card decks and will gravitate toward and use different ones, depending on what calls to me. Another spiritual avenue I use is a spiritual board of directors. I can't recall where I got this idea; it might have been a talk by Wayne Dyer, or an interview of someone else. If you consider that we are all connected to each other's spirit, alive or dead, we have the ability to communicate with and access that intelligence. In my mind, I will call on my board of directors when I want to get out of my own head and get some external input. Sometimes the seats at the table are occupied by different "directors." My current board consists of Wayne Dyer, Fred Rogers (Mr. Rogers from *Mister Rogers' Neighborhood* on PBS), Louise Hay, my father, Eckhart Tolle, and Oprah Winfrey (the latter two are still alive, at this writing).

Peggy, who works as a data security manager for a major insurer and is also an author and a yoga teacher, finds traveling to be a huge source of inspiration. There are many facets to Peggy's life: she formerly served in the Air Force, and she is a breast cancer survivor. She and her husband Rick have six children (four of his from a former marriage and two of Peggy's from a former marriage) and five grandchildren. After her divorce from her first husband, she reconnected with Rick, who was her first boyfriend twenty-five years earlier. While her home base is in New Hampshire, she spends the winters in Key West, Florida (her job allows her to work remotely), and has a daughter and grandson in Ireland. She says, "Travelling feeds my sense of adventure and fuels my creative side. It's like getting out of my own little world and exploring something different. Being on the water in Key West is incredibly calming: the colors of blue shimmer as the sunlight bounces off the water's surface. I lose track of time when I'm paddling around the Flats, I'm immersed in nature around the mangroves."

Making the space for inspiring energy often opens the door to mental clarity. In fact, during one winter in Key West, Rick asked Peggy, "Do you miss your stuff?" Peggy said no. This question popped up during a discussion of two acquaintances who had recently died relatively young, one at sixty-one, the other at fifty-five. Further, Peggy was feeling a heavy negative energy with her job and didn't want to be tied to a particular job in order to pay living expenses. She wondered if they could significantly reduce their daily cost of living in their New Hampshire home.

After returning to New Hampshire that winter, Peggy and Rick decided to downsize. They sold their home five months after their "stuff" discussion. They now live in their new smaller home that will allow them to cut their home occupancy costs in half. Peggy now feels the energy as bright and happy – blended with some hectic rushing and fun – and can see the light at the end of the tunnel. It's eased the energy load for her around money and possessions. "Now we have the house to take us from our fifties into our seventies or eighties. People in their seventies and eighties are telling us they wish they did what we are doing now. I'm done consuming to the extent I did in the past. As we prepared to put our home up for sale, heaving stuff into the dumpster in our driveway was cathartic. I donated over 400 books, and re-homed my Polish pottery to serious collectors. I feel like this change will further help me to live life on my own terms: we'll be able to travel a lot more and travel whenever we want. Every time a major life decision happens, I find I redefine my terms upon life. For years, I've resonated with the T.S. Eliot quote from his book *The Confidential Clerk*: 'If you are unwilling to impose your own terms upon life, then you must be willing to accept what life offers you.'"

Lauraly, who works as a retail manager and is single, gets inspiration from the children in her life. "I always wanted my own children but it never happened. I enjoy being around the kids: my nieces, nephews and the other little ones that call me 'Auntie.' They make me laugh with their honesty and energy. It's refreshing to spend time with them. There is no better way to view the world than through the eyes of a child."

Amy has two young children, works for a nonprofit, and has made several deliberate choices in how she approaches her life. "My girls (ages ten and a half and six) are my biggest source of inspiration. For them, I am modeling being a successful professional woman and trying to balance work and home. Knowing that my husband and I are collaborating to provide some things to them that we didn't have growing up, but we feel are important, keeps me motivated. Also, my undergraduate alma mater, Simmons College, is a big source of inspiration. Whenever I go back to campus, usually in a volunteer role, I see so many young women who are fulfilling the vision of John Simmons, the founder of the college: that women should be able to earn independent livelihoods and lead meaningful lives. Whatever one interprets a 'meaningful life' to be is up to the individual. It's important that women have the opportunity to choose and create such a life."

Amy continues: "I think I have finally given up the notion of having it all. I can't have a spotless house and cook fancy meals and work forty hours a week and be present for my kids and volunteer and try to go to the gym and go on exotic vacations. Something usually gives. And that's okay (though I usually have to remind myself that it is okay). At this time in my career, I could be the director of development rather than the second in command, but my current job affords me more time with my kids and doesn't require much travel. I could even be making a higher salary elsewhere with more prestige, but this works for me. Plus, I like my job and feel like I am doing meaningful work. I also have worked for nonprofits since I graduated college and volunteer when I can for various organizations. That stems from a Jewish concept of *tikkun olam*, which translates to 'repairing the world.' I feel like we all have to do our part to give back in some way. That social justice framework is meaningful to me."

Jen, who works as an occupational therapist and is married with two high school-age children, was inspired by both reading the *Life is Good* book and meeting one of the authors (and company founders), John Jacobs. A major emphasis of that book is optimism: one noteworthy chapter presents the perspective that we "get to" do things each day versus "have to." Jen felt this view reframes a situation in a way that brings gratitude to the forefront for our ability or opportunity to do a task. On the day I interviewed Jen, she said that line of thinking is getting her through her housecleaning! Her lens: "How lucky I am that I am healthy and mobile: I get to clean my house myself." This is a strong example of how inspiring energy feeds emotional energy.

Jodi, an oncology social worker at Massachusetts General Hospital, says, "I'm inspired by the compassion I see in my colleagues. They make me want to do better in my clinical work every day. Processing cases and connecting with them is so important to me. It helps me stay grounded in this crazy (often depressing) career. I regularly attend CEU courses to learn from my colleagues. Hearing their personal and professional insights is so beneficial and keeps me inspired because this work is hard."

If I were to ask you what inspires *you*, how would you answer? As we close this chapter, think about the energy buckets you most want to address at this time.

EXERCISE TWO: SELF-ASSESS YOUR ENERGY BUCKETS
Review the definitions of the four different buckets of energy. Give each bucket a rating from 1 to 10 (where 1 is poor and 10 is excellent) on its level of quality in your life. Now revisit your Wellness Vision and energizing story and decide which energy buckets you want to maintain at their present "fill level" and where you want to amp things up in order to attain that Wellness Vision and story. Review your responses in Chapter 2's *Exercise Two: Perform an Energy Evaluation.* For each energy bucket that you want to focus on at this time, or the energy infusers, what doing and being actions are you ready to commit to? We're taking what you created back in Chapter 2 and digging down to another level of detail. Use the personal examples in this chapter, as well as the many tips shared, to create your own list.

Which of your energy drains are you ready to release by either reducing, removing, or responding to them differently? In fact, to make this easy to remember, I call this concept the "Three R Rescue" – Remove, Reduce and

Respond. Once you identify what is causing your energy to drain, ask yourself if it's possible to remove that trigger. If yes, then take the appropriate action and/or make a plan to do so. If removing the trigger isn't viable, then determine whether reducing the trigger (either cutting back the trigger itself or reducing your exposure to it) is a workable approach. If neither removing nor reducing is possible, or you're able to reduce it yet it's still causing you to feel drained, your final option is to change your response to the trigger. Note that there will likely be some overlap in some do's and be's in how you choose to address each part, and some actions and ways of being may impact more than one piece.

ENERGY BUCKETS	ENERGY INFUSERS TO KEEP OR ADD	ENERGY DRAINS TO REDUCE, REMOVE, OR RESPOND TO DIFFERENTLY
Physical		
Emotional		

ENERGY BUCKETS	ENERGY INFUSERS TO KEEP OR ADD	ENERGY DRAINS TO REDUCE, REMOVE, OR RESPOND TO DIFFERENTLY
Mental		
Spiritual		

We've now looked at one aspect of energy sources in your Burnout-Proofing Dashboard. With the detailed knowledge of the energy buckets now in hand, in the next chapter let's delve further into more energy elements available to you.

CHAPTER EIGHT

Maximize Your Energy Intelligence

"Life isn't about finding pieces of a puzzle. It's about creating and putting those exceptional pieces together."
~ GLENN VAN DEKKEN

Beyond the spaces and energy buckets explored in Chapters 4 and 7, there are additional nuances. There are also ways to conserve your energy, and hidden ways energy leeches from you. This chapter addresses those aspects of energy to further enhance your energy intelligence, and as such, strengthen your ability to avoid burnout.

One of my main reasons for writing this book is to give professional women a model of a way to function that's not "go-go-go" all the time. We know the nonstop nature of this way of operating can deplete your energy, in the absence of routine renewal. The lack of such recovery can negatively impact all four energy buckets (physical, emotional, mental, and spiritual). That's why I'm talking about the importance of giving yourself breaks.

Brain Breaks

Don't wait for the next weekend or vacation for recovery time (although those are fantastic) – be sure to also build routine breaks into your days. At a minimum, you'll get physical and mental energetic benefits from doing so. Work at a desk or spend a fair amount of time commuting each day for your job? That sitting time works against you. Plodding through work, for hours on end, eating lunch at your desk (if you eat at all), barely getting up to use the restroom? You're doing your brain (and your productivity and quality of work) no favors.

Instead of constantly being engrossed in your work, move and give yourself consistent brain breaks. Doing so helps you counter the toxic effects on your brain and heart from sitting too long, and also helps you be more creative and energized. Further, a variety of research has shown that when we take a brain break every sixty to ninety minutes, it helps us restore our focus.

When you take a brain break, which initially can be anywhere from two to ten minutes, you allow your mind to wander, which allows the brain to keep solving problems in the background. Consider the ideas that pop into your head when you're in the shower, as discussed in Chapter 4. Taking brain breaks is a way of consciously giving your brain such breathing space.

Imagine your brain has a gas gauge like the one in your vehicle: ideally you want to take a brain break before you feel like your brain energy is on empty. You might find you need shorter brain breaks before lunch and longer brain breaks after lunch. Think of a brain break as a way to move and recharge your brain before its energy gets too low.

What are some possible actions for you to take on a brain break?

- Get up and look out a window in a different area from where your desk is located.
- Climb stairs.
- Take a coffee or tea break.
- Mindfully walk outside (notice how your feet feel in your shoes, your posture, what you're doing with your hands, your breathing, sights, sounds, smells).

Work from home? Other options include:

- Play with your pet.
- Take out the garbage.
- Check your postal mail.
- Do a load of laundry.
- Empty the dishwasher.
- Water some plants.
- Vacuum one room.
- Do yoga poses and/or stretches.

In the breaks I took during writing one day, I managed to get in three loads of laundry, enjoy my lunch, and have a nice coffee break with some wonderful Turkish figs. I also fit in a walking stint during one break, to catch some outdoor air and sunshine before the day's sunset.

Sleep

Sleep impacts your physical, mental and emotional energy. I see sleep challenges increasingly pop up in my client work, whether from a quality and/or quantity perspective. First, on the quantity front, get a decent number of hours of sleep: aim for seven to eight hours every night. I can hear some of you asking now, if you're not in that place – *how* do I make this happen? Barring clinical issues that can disrupt sleep (e.g., depression/anxiety, insomnia, sleep apnea, pain, restless leg syndrome), it's deciding and committing to when to wind down, and sleeping in an environment conducive to restful slumber.

Experiment with time frames and boundaries (more on boundaries in Chapter 9). Play with the time frame to find your optimum range and stick to it as many nights of the week as possible. Do something relaxing before going to bed (take a bath, read an inspiring work), instead of watching the news or looking at screens. If you share a household or bed with someone else, reach agreement and get support on wind-down time and your shared sleep environment. Wind-down time might include changing into sleepwear (if you haven't already done so earlier), avoiding screens (TV, phone, and other electronic devices) at least an hour before bed, and being in a relaxing manner that prepares you for rest. If you have a TV in your bedroom, consider moving it to a different room.

Sleep quality also depends on your environment. Sleep on a supportive mattress in a room that's comfortably cool, quiet, with no light sources (and yes, that includes your phone). Room-darkening shades can help, and if that's not possible, sleep masks are a workable alternative. If you use an alarm clock, turn the clock's face away from you, or consider using your phone as an alarm clock, facedown, as far away from your bed as possible.

Nutrient-Dense Foods

In general, I find that focusing on primarily eating food that makes you more healthy (versus less healthy) as part of a long-term sustainable lifestyle works better than temporary "diets." Emphasize consuming real, nutrient-dense whole food (instead of processed foods) more often than not.

Margot reached a place where she saw that sugar was not doing her any favors and decided to remove it from her life. She was able to lose and keep off fifty pounds by making food choices that best support her (which, for her, meant going no sugar and super low-carb), along with using her exercise bike daily. This made her become more compassionate toward people struggling or feeling bad about their needs. She now has reached a point of feeling resourceful, rested, calm and creative. She doesn't feel emotionally volatile. Fueling herself in these ways first helps her be the resource she wants to be for herself and others.

Notice whether certain foods or beverages affect your energy and sleep. Stay sufficiently hydrated. Various guidelines exist, from at least sixty-four ounces of water daily, to keeping your urine the color of straw, to drinking the amount of water that is half your body weight in ounces. For example, following the last guideline, if you weigh 160 pounds, you would drink eighty ounces of water daily. Check with your physician to see what level of water consumption they recommend for you. Quality nutrition means fueling your brain in a healthy fashion that helps you stay focused, and also supports you physically and emotionally. Instead of relying on caffeine to help sharpen your mental focus, experiment with different combinations of lean protein, vegetables, fruits, whole grains, and healthy fats (either as a meal or a snack at a certain time period before your most important task block, to refuel your brain in the most optimal way). Besides performing the following exercise, seek the advice of a registered dietician to tailor options that work best for your nutritional needs.

EXERCISE ONE: OBSERVE FOOD AND BEVERAGE IMPACT

When was the last time you paid attention to what you were eating or drinking and how that affects your body and mind? Do you feel bloated or have digestive issues after eating certain foods? Do you get headaches? Is it hard for you to concentrate – do you feel foggy in your head? Does your heart race? Do you feel tired/fatigued? Do you feel overly emotional or sad? If you haven't stopped to pay attention to these symptoms, you may be inadvertently letting your food and beverage choices cause energy leaks or barriers for you.

One relatively simple way to start investigating this is to track your food and beverage intake and note how you feel physically, emotionally and mentally before and after meals. Include sleep patterns, and the environment you're in (e.g., sitting at a dining room table, standing over the kitchen counter, eating on the couch, in bed, or in your car). After you've tracked this for two to four weeks, if certain items stand out, you could then test *temporarily* eliminating certain foods or ingredients to see if that changes your symptoms. Again, log what you eat and how you feel. If you eliminate several foods at once, keep them out of your diet for twenty-one to thirty days, and then add each food item back one at a time, to see if and how your body reacts. Do this exercise in conjunction with a registered dietician, to ensure that, no matter what the outcomes, you ultimately eat in a way that gives you the appropriate nutrition and satiety for your optimal health.

Energy Leaks

Emotional or mental buckets can spring energy leaks, in the form of worrying, holding onto past regrets or grudges, procrastinating, getting poor quality/quantity of sleep, or engaging in analysis paralysis, which I'll define shortly. Energy leaks can spring from physical clutter in all its forms. Mental clutter creates different forms of "busy mind," where our thoughts and/or emotions run the show and take us away from being present. Being in this place can also cause us to rush around and put ourselves in a chronic state of frenzy.

Let's begin with **worry**, which is a story – a concern about what might happen. This could be anything from world events, job/financial security, the weather, flying and travel, to a project outcome, someone's reaction to something you say or do, your children's success in school, your relationships, or life. I'm not suggesting that you act recklessly and throw caution to the wind. Instead, I suggest that you pay attention when worrying absorbs your energy and takes over your ability to be present and deal with what's happening now. Use worry as a trigger that reminds you to step back, recognize what's real and true in this moment, and what control or influence you have in the situation. How can you respond in a way that creates energetic space for you, mentally and emotionally?

Procrastination can indirectly be an energetic drain as well. When you postpone acting, your thoughts consume your mind space around taking the next step. Examples include a conversation that you anticipate will be difficult, a task that feels unwieldy, or a medical appointment that you don't want to schedule. Consider the energy involved in perpetually procrastinating that next step. There's the mental energy of revisiting the matter, and/or perhaps doing busywork instead. This one circumstance is causing multiple, repeated energy leaks! Imagine what you could free up by doing, dropping, or delegating the task, or simply taking the next step forward. Maybe you make a phone call or send a message, maybe you ask for help, or maybe you do some research.

Analysis paralysis combines aspects of worry and procrastination. You're endlessly viewing all sides of a decision before going forward, trying to account for all possible outcomes, pros and cons, risks and benefits. Critical thinking is certainly valuable in decision-making; however, not every decision requires the same level of exploration and consideration. Choosing a school, job, or home, or planning a trip requires a different depth of analysis than deciding what to have for dinner tonight. Be discerning about how you use your brain power. Consider whether a choice requires deep and extensive thought and when you can treat it more lightly. Create the space that allows you to hear your intuition, both to help your decision-making and to free up more brain cells in the process. (Refer to Chapter 4 for a variety of options to create this space.)

Clutter. Entire books exist on decluttering. The clutter from papers on your desk or any flat surface, the laundry waiting on your living room couch to be folded, the excess email in your inbox – all these not only take up physical space in your environment but also consume mental space in your head. Items like the clothes you no longer wear and the books you don't need to keep drain energy from you and your surroundings. Increase your mental capacity and "breathing room" by periodically chipping away at the clutter. Block out some time to tackle clutter or hire a professional organizer if necessary, and file, toss, or donate.

Along with the physical stuff, don't forget about the mind clutter: the excess thoughts running in your head. From the to-dos and the "what if" worries to ruminating in analysis paralysis, all these modes that absorb your mind are consuming energy and taking up brain space. The idea is to avoid getting caught up in the swirl of this type of brain activity. Give yourself an outlet, a release valve of sorts. Document your to-dos and use fear-based thinking and times you find yourself caught up in analyzing decisions as triggers that remind you to step back, give yourself and your brain some space, and choose another mindset or direction that removes you from the clutches of mind chatter. A mindful meditation and/or journaling practice, discussed in Chapter 6, can help you avoid being consumed by these types of thoughts.

Clear the slate on **regrets and grudges**. These are certain types of mind chatter that can drain your mental and emotional energy. Regrets are another version of a story we have about our past. Is there something you can learn from that past experience? Great! Apply that lesson to the now, be grateful for the learning and leave behind your interpretations of what happened. Move forward. You might be holding a grudge toward a friend, family member, coworker, or the person who cut you off in traffic today. *Let it go.* When you're focused on elevating your energy, you don't have room for this sort of negativity. The grudge you're holding is keeping you in an energetic prison. When you choose to release the grudge, you're not letting the other person off the hook, you're unlocking the chains that are holding you back. Why keep punishing yourself this way? You might symbolically wipe the grudge slate clean with a silent message to the person who you feel wronged you, by journaling, or by writing a letter and burning it. Get it out and discharge it.

Avoid rushing. Pace yourself. Leave ample time by overestimating the amount of time you need to complete your tasks so you don't feel rushed and under pressure. Build in buffer time when you can between meetings and appointments.

Donna always gives herself at least a half-hour more than she thinks she needs to get to a client appointment, as traffic and road construction at certain times of the year can be unpredictable. She adds, "I used to feel I wasn't maximizing my time. Leaving extra time now allows me to make my often long drives more peaceful. I know I have plenty of time as opposed to sweating it out for an hour and a half. If and when I get there early, I use that time for a mini meditation break, to return a call, or to journal a few thoughts."

Stressful triggers, and more specifically, *our response to them*, can be another energy leak – emotionally, physically and mentally. Many books are available on coping with and conquering negative stress, and some of the women's stories throughout this book address how they manage stress. In the context of energy intelligence, what I want to emphasize here is creating awareness around (1) what causes you such stress, and (2) what you can do about those culprits. I'm reminded of a wonderful Jon Kabat-Zinn quote: "It is not the stressor itself, but how you perceive it, and how you handle it, that determines whether or not it will lead to stress." Think of this as a form of acceptance, a way of being present with the trigger. How can you accept this trigger and respond to it in a way that best serves your energy? What if this trigger was done for you instead of to you? Possessing inner balance (Chapter 4), self-compassion (Chapter 5), and presence (Chapter 6) also improves your stress responses.

Conserving Energy

Besides figuring out ways to give yourself energy in the four energy buckets (physical, emotional, mental and spiritual), it's also worth addressing ways to conserve your energy, further avoiding energy leaks. If you have a medical condition or chronic illness that depletes your energy, it's also about staying on top of the ways you can preserve your energy. The remaining examples in this chapter are meant to give you ideas on how to conserve energy.

Simplify. First, consider your typical activities during the day and how you can simplify them. What's realistic for you to take on, on a particular day? This may differ day to day, depending on your energy and what's currently on your plate, which is why it's important to check in with yourself on today's reality. Here are some ideas for ways to simplify at home:

MEAL PREPARATION

- [ ] Maximize the meals you can create in a slow cooker, or one-pan meals that make multiple servings that let you cook once and have enough leftovers for future meals. Leftovers can open up lots of time on the back end.

☐ Keep items on hand for quick healthy meals in a pinch, for when you don't have the time or energy to cook. Pantry and fridge/freezer staples can include canned fish or poultry, healthy sausages or hot dogs, eggs, vegetables that work well roasted or in a stir-fry, frittata, or salad.

☐ Think differently about what you may have labeled "breakfast," "lunch" or "dinner" foods. Who says you can't have soup or chicken at breakfast, or an omelet for dinner?

☐ Identify resources for healthy prepared meals for times when it's tricky for you or someone else in your household to cook on a particular day (or you want a break from meal prep), yet you want a decent meal. This can include your local grocer, restaurants, and meal delivery services.

☐ Use your grocer's online ordering and delivery service to minimize shopping trips.

WARDROBE

☐ Each season, sort through and try on your clothing and accessories to identify items to repair, donate or toss, plus identify wardrobe "holes" to fill and keep a list on your phone or small notepad, so you have it with you when shopping.

☐ Focus your wardrobe on basics and foundational pieces, adding accessories and selected trendy items for a bit of fun.

☐ Organize your closet by type of clothing or by outfit to make it easy to choose what to wear for the day.

HOUSEHOLD CHORES

☐ If you have small children, make a game of household chores, so that they will want to help and have fun doing it.

☐ For the younger adults/older children with whom you share a home, groom them for their future independence, and also contributing to a household they share. The list of possibilities is endless, from meal preparation and laundry to yard work and snow removal. Exercise flexibility on minimum standards.

Use a combination of ***planning and delegating***. Let go of feeling that you must do it all or hold exceedingly high standards in every realm. Plan out what you will do, and to whom you can delegate tasks, at work and at home.

This may mean teaching others and adjusting your standards for what is good enough. Prioritize peace and space over having it done your way.

When shopping at brick and mortar stores, ***shop when the stores are less crowded.*** When you go to the grocery store, organize your shopping list so you can shop by aisle. Use online grocery and food delivery services, and online shopping available from other retailers.

Arrange your work environment to easily access frequently used items. This can apply to your desk, to the kitchen, and to your hobby room. Place heavily used objects in locations that minimize over-bending and over-reaching. Consider leaving your most-used gadgets on the desk or kitchen counter.

Don't wait until you are exhausted to rest. Use the brain breaks discussed earlier in this chapter for routine body breaks as well. Avoid getting over-tired.

EXERCISE TWO: COMPLETE YOUR ENERGY PUZZLE

Pull out your Wellness Vision and energizing story and choose the puzzle pieces in this chapter – the nuances, energy leaks and strategies to conserve energy – that most called to you and whose presence or absence will most support you on your path to create your Wellness Vision. List the top five below, completing the energy sources for your Burnout-Proofing Dashboard.

1.

2.

3.

4.

5.

Instituting boundaries is another type of puzzle piece. Because this concept is also tightly intertwined with relationships, I address boundaries further in Chapter 9.

CHAPTER NINE

Cultivate Relationships and Social Connections

"Studies indicate 'social capital' is one of the biggest predictors for health, happiness, and longevity."

~ CECILE ANDREWS

What social outlets do you have, and how are they supporting or detracting from your energy and vitality? What does the space of "me time" versus social time (both online and in person) look like? Having support networks and nurturing interpersonal relationships while setting boundaries as needed collectively enhances our energy and staves off burnout. Set aside the notion that everything rests 100% on your shoulders, and that asking for help is a weakness. Through the stories presented in the first part of this chapter, you will see multiple instances and benefits of building and maintaining a circle of support. When you read a woman's story that resonates for you, journal on the subsequent questions presented.

Cultivate Balanced Relationships

Sheryl, a two-time breast cancer survivor who lives with multiple sclerosis, has found that having a team of people who have her back has been essential. That team consists of her husband, mother, sister, old and new friends – all people she trusts, no matter what. What enables that trust varies, depending on the history. Essentially, she knows that person will be there for her. Sheryl works hard to cultivate relationships, and in doing so, she strives to be the person to them that she wants them to be for her. Specific tactics she uses are as follows:

• Listens intently.

- Sends cards to people.
- When someone is going through a challenge or tough time, she puts reminders in her calendar to make a phone call or send a text to check in and see how they're doing.
- She enjoys communicating over dinner and likes to see people in her close circle as often as possible.
- She schedules phone calls with long-distance friends to catch up.

She gets a sense of being complete, full and happy when giving support. Such relationships have helped keep her sane, and better define who she is. They give her the freedom and space to try out different parts of herself and think about life in different ways. There is a core respect that will be there no matter what, and that allows her to feel safe in being her authentic self. Having this level of concern from and for certain people allows her to feel blessed and lucky on a daily basis with mutual love, support and understanding.

That's not to say there haven't been challenges along the way. Two friends reacted very differently to her cancer diagnoses. Sheryl had a friendship with a woman we'll call Lisa, where Sheryl felt that she herself was always the one who gave more. Yet, Sheryl got enough back from Lisa that there seemed to be a good sense of balance in the relationship. On Sheryl's first diagnosis, Lisa called once after Sheryl's surgery and then Sheryl didn't hear from her for two months, until she received an email from her out of the blue. Receiving this outreach at this late stage left Sheryl hurt and disappointed, and she confronted Lisa about it. They met for brunch, and Sheryl felt neither a connection with nor anger toward her friend. She thought she could forgive Lisa, but couldn't; the get-together confirmed Sheryl's sense of Lisa's selfish and shallow behavior. Sheryl felt Lisa could have reached out any number of ways over that two-month span, but she didn't. Their brunch conversation acknowledged that they each were on completely different wavelengths. As a result, Sheryl "broke up" this friendship. They are still connected on Facebook, since Sheryl wants to be sure this person is okay. She doesn't want to attempt a deeper level of friendship again, because she doesn't want to leave herself open to be hurt that way again; she felt shocked, hurt, depleted and saddened through that ordeal.

Ken had been Sheryl's friend since they were four years old. He knew about Sheryl's second cancer diagnosis yet didn't call her for three months. In fact, Sheryl had finished chemo and started radiation by the time he called. He offered an excuse for why he hadn't called but Sheryl confronted him, saying how disappointed she was that he wasn't there for her during the hardest part of her life. He apologized, cried, and asked for forgiveness. She forgave him and left it for him to contact her. Ken did call her a few weeks later and they've remained in contact since then. Sheryl felt alive, invincible and empowered in speaking up for what was true for her, because she knew she couldn't let it go without saying something. Yes, there was a risk that she could have lost this friendship, but her circumstances heightened her need to know that he was going to be there for her, no matter what.

Questions for you:

- Who do you know you can count on, if you were to experience a crisis?
- Which relationships have a balance of give and take that is acceptable to you?
- Which relationships feel one-sided?
- If you have one-sided relationships, determine which ones you want to keep, and what side needs work (yours or the other person's) to make it more balanced. Have a conversation with that person to speak up for what you will change and/or what you need from them.
- For the one-sided relationships that you're ready to dissolve, decide how you feel it would be appropriate to end or leave them.

Be a Resource

For Margot, a professional mediator, "there's nothing that makes me feel better than being helpful. It resonates through my being. It's harmony. The more I feel compassionate, resourceful and helpful to family, friends and clients, the more I want to keep doing these actions." That's not to say that Margot puts herself last; that was the behavior her mother modeled. Margot fuels herself first with the exercise and eating habits that keep her healthy; this gives her the energy she needs to feel empowered as a resource in all her interactions, both personal and professional.

Questions for you:

- Who do you care for, serve or otherwise help in your life, in and out of work?
- What fuel do you need to be effective in those roles?

Awareness of Other's Energies in Social Settings

Erin is in her late forties and co-owns her chocolate manufacturing and gift business with her husband. In the aftermath of the 2016 presidential election, she found she had to transition out of former social relationships into new ones where she is around like-minded people. She wanted mentors with positive energy and recognized the need to separate from certain people who looked at life in a negative way. She also wanted to stop comparing herself to others.

Erin felt she didn't have enough "armor" for some of the negative energy of others, and she knew she couldn't control other people's feelings. A group of friends began to exclude her on social media and in person based on political and other social differences. A childhood friend always wanted to "party." But what mattered to Erin was different now; she wanted to focus on the reality of her life, her business and her three children (ages seventeen, fifteen, and ten). Her top priorities now are advancing herself, her company and her children. "My life is my family and business, and everything else has to be positive." She landed in a Bible-supported weight loss group through which she has adopted a fifteen-minute morning practice of reading scripture. That focus on scripture has given her clarity (e.g., Romans: "Do not conform to the patterns of this world."). Working out and using weights after reading scripture helps her process the message of the day. This ritual has helped her keep her emotions in check in various political and social situations.

Questions for you:

- Who exudes positive energy and a vibe of camaraderie when in your presence?
- Who gives off negative energy, is confrontational and/or often tries to one-up or compete with others?

Grace, Courage, Humor

Barbara, an editor in her mid-fifties who is a divorced mom of two young adult children, operates under the mantra that there's very little we can control, except our response to things. Are you going to be angry, emotional, or look on the bright side? A few years back, a man she was dating died suddenly. She was overwhelmed by the number of people who sent flowers and food. To help her cope with this loss, she wrote a lot about it and went on walks in the woods with her dog. As a result, her perspective on and relationship with life and death is different today. She makes a point of telling her two sons every day that she loves them. After this major life event of losing someone, her question wasn't why she's still living her life but *how* she will live her life. How do you view the world and live your life now?

One of the realities Barbara has come to grips with is that the people who trigger you are the people whose story you need to understand. In her former job, she was up for a promotion, and her manager was threatened by her. She got a bad performance review, and walked out in the middle of it to avoid bursting into tears. She ultimately requested an equitable separation from the employer, which she got, with no drama. What she understood about her manager was that she was insecure and manipulative. Barbara left that employer knowing that the problem was her manager's "stuff" and not to take it personally. After leaving, she applied for other jobs with renewed vigor. She reached out to a colleague she'd known for thirty years, and that person invited her to join their company, which is how she landed her current role.

Barbara has learned to surround herself with positive people and gently release others from her life. She now has a tattoo with the mantra "Grace, Courage, Humor." To her, grace means taking the high road and staying classy. Courage means being positive and sensitive, possessing the strength to be empathetic, have compassion and forgiveness, and to draw the line and set boundaries that help her let go of negativity. Humor means the ability to generate laughter from anything.

Questions for you:

- Who in your life pushes your buttons? What might they have to teach you? What could you learn from/about them?

- Who needs to be gently released from your life?
- Who do you appreciate and/or love in your life, and when was the last time you explicitly told them that?

Quality Attention for Key People

Lauren had a feeling she was doing too much. She found it so easy to say yes all the time, since she could see everything she was able to do and wanted to do it all. She gradually realized she wasn't taking the time to evaluate requests for her time. Before she became a parent to two children, she didn't think much would change once she had a family. However, she eventually saw how the prestige associated with her job wasn't enough to fulfill her, and she felt pulled in different directions and that her kids needed her time and energy. She ultimately felt that her priority was to be able to be deeply present with her husband and children when she was with them (instead of feeling exhausted or that her mind was elsewhere). She went from being executive director of a business association in Boston to a role as the executive director of her town's Chamber of Commerce. Taking that position was the first step in moving away from being spread too thin and being pushed too much.

By the same token, Lauren and her husband make a conscious effort to avoid over-scheduling their kids with too many activities. She says, "I realize we all have limitations and I am okay with that." She takes time on the weekends to go for a run alone, as she's found that helps re-energize how she is with her husband. "I used to think he should know I need to run alone. I ultimately learned how to say what I need. When I recognize what I need, ask for help and accept it, this has translated into better times with my husband and our kids."

Putting family at the top of her priority list includes maximizing the quality conversation at dinners she shares with them. As Lauren explains, "Most nights, once the four of us sit down for dinner, everyone gets to share a highlight of their day and what they are thankful for. It has become such a part of our evenings that my four-year-old will remind us if we forget and dig right in. The kids don't care if we're eating homemade meatballs or frozen pizza, so if we can't get a gourmet meal on the table we don't sweat it. It's more about sitting down and being present all at once, the four of us." Instead of scheduling dinners with friends or colleagues to catch up, she'll often suggest that they meet to take a walk instead. She's found it helpful to have conversations with other women who've chosen to arrange their life around what's important to them, especially in a society where we are bombarded by messages about how we're "supposed" to be.

Questions for you:

- If you consider what and who is important in your life, and how you're currently spending your time and energy, how well-aligned are those two aspects? What must you adjust to bring these two closer together?
- Where do you need to set boundaries?

Reminder: answer the questions paired with any of the previous stories that resonated for you.

Assemble Your "A" Team and Regroup to Reprioritize Relationships

While you can go it alone, doing so is not necessary. Plus, there are so many upsides to having other human beings in your sphere who support you. Wherever you are on the spectrum of energy (from being depleted to feeling lively), it's helpful to have people around you who see the real you. They know you at your best, and they can tell when something is off in your tone, appearance or the energy you're putting out there. We can all use others in our lives whom we can trust to call us out, gently and compassionately.

Who is your support or "A" team? Who is your tribe, squad or community? Who are the professional and personal contacts in your circle who can help you shine? Who will encourage or otherwise assist you in attaining your optimal energy and vitality? List names and specify how they can support you in the following table.

YOUR "A" TEAM

FAMILY AND FRIENDS	COWORKERS, MENTORS AND CONNECTORS	PROFESSIONAL SERVICE PROVIDERS
		health coach, personal trainer, fitness instructor
		massage therapist
		physicians, registered dietician, other healthcare professionals
		dentist
		accountant
		financial planner/advisor
		attorneys (at least an estate planning attorney; build relationships with other specialties as needed)
		professional organizer

Reevaluate Your Commitments and Relationships

Do you dread attending certain long-standing meetings? Decide what's necessary to preserve your wellness. Do you have a friend or family member who is an energy vampire, someone who drains the life right out of you? Someone who stirs the pot to create drama? Protect your own well-being around them by setting appropriate boundaries. If necessary, wean yourself away from them or cut the time you spend with them as much as possible. On the other hand, if you feel alive and positive in certain people's company, keep hanging around them! You may find you're able to categorize your most prominent relationships in three different tiers:

- **THE TIER 1 PEOPLE** offer unending support. They see and accept the authentic you, from flaws to virtues, and always have your back.

- **THE TIER 2 PEOPLE** are not at the top of your list of people to whom you'd initially reach out, and they may be in more of a neutral zone of supporting/not supporting you. They may not be your closest contacts, and while you enjoy their company, you don't know them as deeply as the Tier 1 folks. They might even be relationships that were previously closer, but perhaps your priorities, interests, and/or lives have changed in ways that have resulted in you growing apart.

- **THE TIER 3 PEOPLE** may try to nudge you away from any new direction you may take for the betterment of your health, or even sabotage your efforts.

Identify the Tier 1, 2, and 3 people that come to mind as you read the above descriptions. What are you doing to cultivate the Tier 1 relationships? How have you conveyed to these people the ways they can best support you? Plant and nurture those seeds as part of the fabric of your life; avoid waiting until you're in crisis. In general, go for quality over quantity.

On the Tier 2 relationships, which ones have the possibility of moving into the Tier 1 space? Who could you envision sharing your goals for energized burnout-proof living and having them respond by either joining you or otherwise supporting you in that quest? For the Tier 1 and 2 people that are on your

"A" team, identify them as such in the Your "A" Team table. With respect to the Tier 3 relationships, think about who needs to be released, or with whom you need to have a conversation to express the type of support you need from them (someone with whom you share your home, a family member, or coworker).

Setting Boundaries: Your Compass

For some of us, the idea of instituting boundaries can initially carry a negative connotation. We may think that having boundaries means feeling closed off, or the notion of boundaries generates a sense of separation. However, one synonym for "boundary" perfectly fits the message I want to convey in this section: "compass." Truly, setting boundaries furnishes you with a compass that points toward what you want to accomplish, what's a priority for you.

We each have seven days a week, with twenty-four hours in each day. Getting the most from each day is a balance of how we spend our time and include ways of doing and being that generate energy and allow us to renew our energy. The more purposeful, focused and intentional we are in our choices and the better we feel energetically, the more likely we will grant ourselves permission to focus on what is significant to us.

In or out of work, with family or friends, setting boundaries enables you to realign and recommit to what's most valuable to you. Without boundaries, there is a tendency to fall into the habit of responding to the whims of others, bumbling along, and/or wishing for time to open up to address your needs and wants. Delaying your needs and wants, saying yes to someone when your instinct tells you to say no, or being in a situation where you feel used and drained instead of utilized and exhilarated builds resentment. Unresolved resentment is negative energy that weighs you down.

Setting boundaries gives you the freedom and space to make choices that you value.

Where do you begin?

Decide on what you want. If you had more time and energy on a regular basis, how would you want to use those additional resources? Once you've declared what you want, articulate why it's important to you. Revisit your Wellness Vision for these qualities. This sets the direction and motivation for your compass.

From there, choose one or more of the following tactics to put into place:

☐ **Set a boundary on emails, phone calls, and texting.** Consider conducting this type of communication only between 8 a.m. and 8 p.m., for example. You might also use task-blocking, as discussed in Chapter 7, to allocate specific blocks of your day for these tasks.

☐ **At home, look for opportunities to partner with, lean on and delegate** to those with whom you live, whether it's a roommate, spouse, or children. What can be delegated or shared? Household chores, food preparation, table setting and cleanup, laundry. Also consider outside resources such as online food ordering and delivery, or cleaning services.

☐ **Assess incoming information.** This is everything from snail mail to email. What newsletters are no longer aligned with your priorities? What distribution lists can you be removed from? What organizations are no longer relevant to you? On social media, do you have criteria for those you follow, friend and link to? If not, consider setting up criteria for your connections and sticking to them. Periodically review your contacts for pruning.

☐ **Insert hard stops to end your work day.** If you find long days at work are cutting into your personal life, set limits. Perhaps there are two or three days a week you work only until 5 or 6 p.m., so that you can see your child's game or get to that exercise class. Can you regularly work from home, and reallocate the time spent commuting to doing something else you value?

☐ **Add "no" and "can I get back to you?" to your vocabulary**, especially if you often find yourself immediately saying "yes" to other people's invitations and requests. View "no" as a way of taking a stand for using your time, space and energy for what is essential to and a priority for you. "Can I get back to you" grants you some time to weigh the impact of your answer and how it helps or detracts from your Wellness Vision and intentions to avoid burnout. If you're always saying "yes" to everyone else, you're likely addressing someone else's priorities and delaying focusing on yours. When you have an open slot in your calendar and someone asks you to fill it, measure the worth of this opportunity against your values and the expense of your space, time and energy.

☐ **Evaluate your volunteer commitments.** What activities still resonate with you and what feels like a chore? Remove the "chores" from your plate.

☐ **Do you have a 24/7 open-door policy? Reevaluate that way of being.** Block out appointments with yourself for when you need to plan, renew, create, strategize, think, and/or ground yourself.

Network Authentically

I often hear from solo entrepreneur women, or those who work from home or live alone, that isolation can be a problem. Surprisingly, I'm not going to suggest starting a conversation with a complete stranger at a business networking event. My tips are more intended to get you out and connected in person with other human beings. If conversation naturally unfolds, go for it.

It can be so easy and comfortable to stay indoors, especially with technology and the advances in online social networking. I'm encouraging you to branch out a bit, and reap the benefits of being around other people. I'm personally not a fan of huge crowds, so the tips below are consistent with that preference. Choose those you'd like to test out.

CONNECT AROUND INTERESTS:

☐ Find and try out groups in your area that share your interest. Meetup is one place to find groups based on common interests.

☐ Attend a talk at your local library, or a book signing at a bookstore.

☐ Enroll in a class at a community college or through an adult education center.

☐ Explore a new artistic interest by taking a class at a craft store or local makerspace.

☐ Volunteer for a cause close to your heart. Participate in a fundraising event.

LOCAL FLAVOR:

☐ Be a tourist in your own backyard. Take a tour, visit historical sites and/or a local museum.

☐ In warmer seasons/climates, many communities have outdoor concerts, music festivals, and outdoor movies. Check them out!

AROUND FOOD:

☐ Host or attend a potluck cookout.

☐ Think of a friend or coworker you haven't seen in a while. Contact them to catch up over coffee or a meal.

☐ Dine at a restaurant with outdoor dining and good opportunities for people-watching.

☐ Attend a local wine or beer tasting at your favorite shop.

☐ Visit a farmers market.

OLD-FASHIONED FUN:

☐ Watch a child's baseball game.

☐ Patronize mom-and-pop restaurants, coffee shops, and other small businesses. Get to know the owners.

EXPLORE:

☐ Take a day trip to explore another city or town. Your local AAA office, local news programs, magazines, and Chamber of Commerce websites may have some destination ideas, as well as sites like TripAdvisor, Groupon and LivingSocial.

☐ Walk on the beach or around a lake.

☐ Hike or bike on trails.

Your Relationship with Yourself

"You will be with you longer than anyone else on the planet. Why not make it a good relationship?"

~ Louise Hay

If you haven't already read Chapter 5, or you're struggling with being kind and respectful toward yourself, make reading that chapter your next step.

Let's also address where we place ourselves on the priority list. All too often, I hear women speaking of putting themselves last. This way of being tends to be a long-term, ingrained habit. We could look at the multiple aspects at play here, including what was modeled by our parents and other adults in our life growing up, self-worth, the identity and expectations we've held for ourselves, managing our time, and feeling like this is part of what it means to be a caregiver and/or in the sandwich generation.

Re-read your energizing story from Chapter 1. Just as you select the people you keep in your life and set expectations around how they'll satisfy your needs and wants, take the time to look within and honor yourself and the reality of living your energizing story. We teach others how we want to be treated by how we take care of ourselves, including recognizing that we can't effectively operate on empty. In fact, running on no or low fuel is part of what runs us into the ground. If your relationship with yourself is not currently at the Tier 1 level, what steps can you take to move in that direction?

Reflect on the entirety of this chapter, and choose three to five aspects of relationships and social connections to make your main focus at this time. Again, revisit your Wellness Vision and energizing story for what will best support you.

1.

2.

3.

4.

5.

Now is the time to take a stand and be your own best advocate for burnout-proof living. How will you care for yourself in your inner balance (Chapter 4), acceptance and compassion (Chapter 5), being present (Chapter 6), energy management principles (Chapters 7 and 8), and relationships and boundary-setting (this chapter)?

If you're reading the chapters in this book sequentially, this is the final chapter that addresses the various elements of the Burnout-Proofing Dashboard. In the next chapter, you'll assemble all the pieces you selected as you moved through the twists and turns of your path through *Ignition*, into an action plan for burnout-proof living.

Part Three:
Blast Off and Shine

CHAPTER TEN

Ignite Burnout-Proof Patterns

"Discipline is choosing between what you want now and what you want most."

~ AUGUSTA F. KANTRA

Y ou likely picked up this book initially because you want to possess more energy and vitality in order to be a certain way or do particular things (or do them better). You may have been concerned about burnout: either feeling like you are already in it or heading in that direction. Now it's time for the rubber to meet the road: let's create your action plan to ignite new habits or patterns that keep you energized and away from burnout.

As you've progressed through *Ignition*'s stories, exercises, tips, and questions, you've been reviewing your options in your chosen essential areas for enhancing your energy and vitality. You may have even selected or tested out ways to create inner balance and compassion, be present, fuel up, maintain steady energy, and connect. Consistently functioning with these elements increases your burnout-proof abilities in all aspects of your life. At this point, let's transition from play to actual implementation.

That doesn't mean the fun and experimentation stops. In fact, I encourage you to consciously bring optimism to this process. What might it be like for you to be joyful while simultaneously committing to keeping your energy fires stoked? What will help you stay resilient in the face of the inevitable bumps and even brick walls that appear in your path along the way?

Where previous chapters in *Ignition* included stories about other women, the remainder of the book is all about you. It's time to choose the details from your selected Burnout-Proofing Dashboard elements that you want to prioritize and bring into your life for at least the next ninety days. These habits will likely be a mix of doing and being patterns: a blend of actions (new to-dos or actions to do differently), ways of being (new perspectives, attitudes, and approaches), the energy leaks you want to plug up or minimize, as well as the relationships you want to foster and those you want to let go of. Dig out your notes. Review your responses to questions, the outcomes of the exercises or tips you played with, and what you highlighted with interest. We're now going to prioritize and assemble those pieces into building blocks to create your ninety-day action plan.

REVIEW (AND, IF NECESSARY, ADJUST) YOUR DESTINATION

1. Review your Wellness Vision, big whys, and your foundations (strengths, energizing story, and energy infusers).

2. Choose a date up to nine to twelve months from now, by which you will attain your Wellness Vision: your ways of being and doing to live who and what you want to be, in a burnout-proof manner.

3. Decide whether your energizing story and/or Wellness Vision needs any further tweaking to be stated in the most clear and compelling way to ignite and pull you forward, based on your readings from Part Two.

4. Write out your updated energizing story below along with the revised Wellness Vision on the next page with the date you selected.

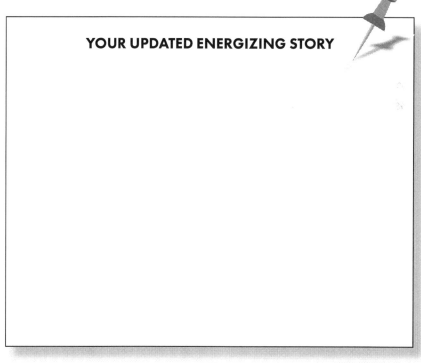

YOUR UPDATED ENERGIZING STORY

YOUR REVISED WELLNESS VISION

By ____/____/_____ I am:
insert date here

IDENTIFY YOUR DOING AND BEING STEPS

With your destination at some point in the future solidified, I now recommend you plan your approach ninety days at a time. Note, that doesn't mean you necessarily fully achieve your Wellness Vision in ninety days. The idea is to consistently make progress and experience benefits by the ninety-day mark that move you closer to your vision. If you get to ninety days and there is more work to be done on completely instilling your burnout-proof living, then conduct this review and planning activity again for the next ninety days. Repeat this ninety-day cycle until you feel your energized lifestyle has become ingrained as your new normal.

How to Complete the Building Blocks

- If you filled out the element building blocks on pages 122 through 126 as you read Part Two, you can now prioritize those pieces you're ready to use for burnout-proof living. Star, check, circle or highlight your priorities for the next ninety days, based on your review in following steps 1-4 on page 119.
- If you have opted to wait until now to complete these building blocks, decide which elements of the Burnout-Proofing Dashboard you want to incorporate over the next ninety days.

If the thought of reviewing or deciding feels overwhelming, keep the following points in mind:

- You might select only one or two dashboard elements as your focus for the next ninety days.
- As a gentle reminder, you don't need to do ALL exercises and/or incorporate every single idea and tip presented in a particular chapter.

Proceed to your selected essential elements' building blocks and select/write down the aspects of each element that you're ready to commit to implementing over the next ninety days. You might list an exercise, tip, action, mindset, behavior, page number, or woman's name/story tidbit as a way to jog your memory. This is *your* plan: document the aspects you want to incorporate in ways that work for you.

Building Block 1
Essential Element: **INNER BALANCE**
Chapter 4

Your Chosen Aspects

Building Block 2
Essential Element: **SELF-COMPASSION**
Chapter 5

Your Chosen Aspects

Building Block 3
Essential Element: **PRESENCE-DRIVEN FOCUS**
Chapter 6

Your Chosen Aspects

Building Block 4
Essential Element: **ENERGY SOURCES**
Chapters 7–8

Your Chosen Aspects

Building Block 5
Essential Element: **SOCIAL/SUPPORT**
Chapter 9

Your Chosen Aspects

What to Keep In Mind to Make Forward Progress

With respect to wellness outcomes and starting or restarting new habits, I find that many people postpone instilling the corresponding actions because they can't do everything as perfectly as they imagined. Or, they get discouraged when they can't do it all right away. Do these statements sound familiar to you?

- I can't work out or meditate for thirty minutes a day.
- I can't eat the proper portion sizes every day at every meal.
- I can't jump from five hours of sleep to eight hours of sleep.

Some people are heavily focused solely on what they need to do instead of also looking at the *being* side: the thinking, the feeling.

Where is it written that we have to be all-or-nothing about our health? Think shades of grey. **What kind of impact could you make by committing to what you *can* do or be now, instead of doing nothing or being the same way?**

Beyond discouragement, guilt is another strong emotion that can impede our forward movement in our self-care. Funny how it's completely okay if we're taking care of others, but heaven forbid we consciously make time to take care of ourselves. This self-care could be anything from "me time" or taking a lunch break away from your desk to using a half- or full day off from work to reset, renew and refresh. If feelings of guilt around redirecting your attention from others to yourself are coming up for you, you're likely carrying some deeply ingrained stories (from your family, culture, workplace or society) about how you feel you should behave. Again, remind yourself of the story you've created to live into now, and bring boldness and conviction to this choice!

We are seriously embarking on habit change. Dr. Michael Merzenich, a leading pioneer in brain plasticity research, in his book, *Soft-Wired*, referenced in a 2015 article on the "Best Brain Possible with Debbie Hampton" website [1] states that, relative to behavior change, "the more something is practiced, the more connections are changed and made to include all elements of the experience (sensory info, movement, cognitive patterns). You can think of it like a 'master controller' being formed for that particular behavior which allows it to be performed with remarkable facility and reliability over time."

1 www.thebestbrainpossible.com/the-10-fundamentals-of-rewiring-your-brain/

Bottom line: neuroscience and creating new brain paths require us to repeatedly practice a new desired behavior. It's helpful to know this going in, so you don't throw in the towel when you don't immediately adopt these new habits 100% of the time. You will stumble, wobble and fall off course. Habit change is not a straight line; it's more like a roller coaster of ups and downs. Revisiting your big whys and approaches to navigating the expected hurdles will help you recommit when you stray off-course from the new habit you're trying to adopt. Expect to be in a mode of continually repeating your desired new patterns, amidst some veering off-track, until you've created new pathways and instilled new rituals of energizing behavior.

Reviewing, pondering and/or playing with the concepts in this book might have your ego working on overdrive with all kinds of worry, warning or otherwise disempowering self-talk. Gently, lovingly and repeatedly remind yourself of the new script you've written and what routines you are now living into.

CREATE NINETY-DAY BEHAVIORAL GOALS

You've prioritized the Burnout-Proofing Dashboard elements and identified their details you intend to incorporate over the next ninety days. Now, define the corresponding habits you will instill in terms of lifestyle goals for you to achieve in the next ninety days. What feels attainable and what would give you an initial energetic lift if you had those principles in place three months from now? What practices are you demonstrating? What is your mindset and outlook? What rituals do you have in place? Convert that into three to five specific, measurable, action-oriented and realistic behavioral goals that you can attain in ninety days' time.

As an example, note that "I have lost weight" or "I have lost five pounds" does not meet the criteria above. If reaching a specific weight is part of your Wellness Vision, think about the behaviors you need to practice in order to attain that weight loss. One option might be: "I am eating two-and-a-half cups of fresh vegetables at least four days a week." If increasing sleep is your intention, you might say: "I am sleeping seven hours nightly at least five nights a week." If giving your brain more powerful fuel is an objective, you might say: "I am taking brain breaks in my work day every ninety minutes, using my phone's timer. I've made a list of possible actions to use during brain breaks, and I will experiment to see which ones work best." If you want to free up more space for what's essential for you to live in a burnout-proof way, you could say, "I've created a criteria for responsibilities to remove from my plate, and am following that criteria in my weekly progress review."

NINETY-DAY GOALS: By ____/____/_____ I am or I have...
insert date here

1.

2.

3.

4.

5.

CREATE THIRTY-DAY BEHAVIORAL GOALS

Let's further drill down into what thirty days from now will look like. Look at the ninety-day goals you've just written down. If you are on your way to those goals, at least one-third of the way there, what would that look like for you in a month's time? You could even think of this in terms of projects to focus on for the next month, and the behaviors required to complete those projects. I find this is where things start to get even more "real," as you zoom into a time frame that's closer to the present. This is your opportunity to deeply commit with iron-clad conviction and start on a solid footing. Decide what's now a priority for you, what's driving your choices, and what support you need to commit and stay on the path. Hashing out all the details might feel tedious, but setting long-term goals alone is not enough to ensure your success. Think of all the people who abandon their New Year's resolutions mere weeks into the process. I want to maximize your chances of being triumphant. Spell out your interim milestone behavioral goals to reach your ninety-day goals.

THIRTY-DAY GOALS: By ____/____/_____ **I am or I have…**
insert date here

1.

2.

3.

4.

5.

CREATE NEXT WEEK'S BEHAVIORAL GOALS

We're here: dealing with what's directly in front of you and what you're ready to put into action over the next seven days. If this makes you even more nervous, ask yourself: **What small step can I take now, to move me toward one of my thirty-day goals?** Here are some starter examples:

- Make my appointment for my annual physical.
- Notice when I'm about to use derogatory terms to describe myself, and instead, choose kinder, more compassionate words.
- Meditate for one minute per day (add one minute a week).
- Go to bed fifteen minutes earlier, or get up fifteen minutes earlier (move increments fifteen minutes each week).
- Reach out to a friend to catch up over the phone, on a walk, or over coffee.
- Look for opportunities to delegate a specific work, home or volunteer task.
- Research exercise workouts that I can stream at home.
- Practice fully listening, without distraction, in conversations with my partner.
- Visit one local gym or Y in my area to get a tour or set up an appointment with a personal trainer at my gym to set up a new routine for my wellness goals.

Begin with small steps, gain traction and build upon these steps as you're inspired.

Write down and schedule three steps you will take <u>this week</u>.

1.

2.

3.

REVIEW WEEKLY AND REPEAT THE CYCLE

Choose a day of the week that you will check in with yourself on your weekly goals. Popular choices are Fridays, Sundays, or Mondays; select what feels right to you. On the day of your check-in each week, you'll celebrate your successes and note what worked well. For any goals that you didn't attain, acknowledge where you struggled and what you learned from that. How can you apply those insights toward creating next week's goals? Use your dashboard to help you continually reassess the type of space, compassion, fuel, presence and support you need. At the thirty-day mark, create your next set of thirty-day goals. Repeat the weekly and monthly review until you reach ninety days, when you also celebrate what you achieved and learned, and decide whether to start another ninety-day cycle to continue progressing toward your Wellness Vision. The next section of this chapter has further instructions to help you think through this process.

EMBRACE STRUCTURE

Rather than just hoping you'll find the time, space and energy for what you just declared for yourself, use this section to help yourself further *design* your life in a way that increases the opportunities for your desired state of energized, burnout-proof living to occur.

> *"When you are able to present your best self to the world, more people will benefit."*
> ~ *Robert Middleton*

What qualities does it take to present your best self?

- **Clarity** about what is important to you, and what you want to achieve;
- **Courage** to do, learn, or get help on what's necessary to attain what you want;
- **Mindset** to optimistically keep moving forward, even when life's happenings may knock you a few steps back or off track; and
- **Energy** to be and act powerfully, positively and efficiently.

These traits generally won't appear on their own, which is where structure comes in. Structure instills the focus, concentration and consciousness needed to routinely implement these qualities. It removes the clutter from your mind and helps you avoid a random and scattered way of operating.

So, to embrace structure, where do you begin?

Initial Planning (repeat as necessary as you create and complete your goals):

1. **Clarify**. Execute the steps described earlier in this chapter to create your Wellness Vision and ninety-day, thirty-day and weekly goals.

2. **Remind yourself** of past accomplishments, and your characteristics that made those accomplishments possible. Review the strengths you identified in Chapter 2. How can you apply these qualities to the goals you want to achieve now?

3. **For each goal that feels too big, document the next one to five steps** it will take to reach that goal.

4. For each step, **identify whether you can perform the step on your own, or whether you need help** from a specific person or other resource to perform this step. In the areas where you need help, if you know the particular resource, contact them. If not, identify as much as you know, and/or where you can go or who can you contact to find that resource. Build an ongoing support list of people and resources.

5. **Structure your day to generate the energy you need to achieve what you want, balanced with the action to get there, and the recovery time to recoup.** Plan cerebral tasks for when you're most "on." Plan routine tasks (email, phone calls, filing), for a specific block of time during each day, to avoid being interruption-driven or distracted.

Execute the Steps:

6. **Have a daily morning routine to "set the table"** and powerfully start the day. Spend at least ten minutes performing one or more activities or rituals that lift you up. Among the many possibilities: exercise/stretching, inspirational reading, prayer, journaling, meditation, visualizing a successful day.

7. **Each day, transfer at least one of the action steps from your weekly goals to your daily to-do list and/or planner.** If the action is something to do, schedule and block it in a way to prevent interruptions. If the action is a way to be, visualize the situation(s) where you intend to demonstrate that behavior.

8. **Set intentions for how you want to be** on a particular day, in a certain situation, while moving through your current task, and/or with a particular human being. What type of energy do you want to exhibit?

9. **Check in with yourself at the end of each day.** Note your accomplishments, what lifted you, and any lessons learned through the day. Make your to-do/to-be/to-feel list for tomorrow, to empty your brain of the next day's actions before going to sleep.

10. After your daily check-in, to help yourself maintain an optimistic outlook, list three to five **things for which you are grateful** today, or at this time in general. Consider keeping a gratitude journal or notebook for just this purpose. During your weekly review, you could also have a happiness jar where you review the week and acknowledge one positive or joyful event. Jot that "win" down on a small piece of paper that

you put in a big jar or large vase (an oversized mason jar works well), and then review all this goodness at the end of the year (or open and review random notes when you need a mental energy boost).

Reward Yourself:

11. **Especially reward the small steps.** Each time you take an action toward your goals, take a moment to celebrate and reward yourself. Reward possibilities include devouring the next chapter in the book you're reading for pleasure, taking a walk around the block, or calling a friend for a fifteen-minute minute catch-up chat.

~~~~~~~~~~~~~~~~~~~~

With your plan now crafted, and further ideas for solidifying these new changes, you might already be concerned about how you stay on the path. We'll address that in the next chapter.

CHAPTER ELEVEN

Negotiate Hurdles Along the Way

"I think of them as speed bumps instead of roadblocks. Just a
minor delay to get me over the hump on the highway to my
dreams. You never know the things you might see if you slow
down on your journey so you can learn and enjoy the moments."
~ MICHELLE COLON-JOHNSON

It's not enough to have goals, a well-thought-out plan, and a structure for following the plan. Life happens, with many unexpected twists and turns. When the stumbling blocks pop up, use them as challenges to overcome, instead of reasons to give up. Continue your sense of play and working with this flow of life instead of letting what seems like a barricade completely derail you. Turn to this chapter any time you feel you've hit a wall or fallen off track in weaving your desired burnout-proofing elements into your life. Here you'll find reminders for navigating around the various speed bumps you may encounter, allowing yourself to regroup and make forward progress.

Examples of snags with the potential to thwart our efforts include:

- Procrastination
- Giving up prematurely
- Self-sabotage
- Perfectionism

How you treat your response to any of these behaviors or situations impacts your success in making your desired changes. Getting angry or berating yourself about it isn't conducive to forward progress.

Some of the behaviors listed above may be long-term habits of yours. What if you befriended or were even amused by such habits that have been barriers for you? Knowing that a certain habit tends to appear for you, what can you do to head it off at the pass? How can you dance, play, and move with it, instead of trying to banish and punish it (and yourself)?

Turning Procrastination Around

Take procrastination as an example. If you have habitually procrastinated, that's where your brain is going to take you first. Why? Because it's the default behavior etched in your brain's current neural pathways. In an April 2015 *Fast Company* magazine article[1] titled "What It Takes to Change Your Brain's Patterns After Age 25," Deborah Ancona, a professor of management and organizational studies at MIT, states that "It turns out that we, as human beings, develop neural pathways, and the more we use those neural pathways over years and years and years, they become very stuck and deeply embedded, moving into deeper portions of the brain." However, with repetition of your selected new approaches, you can create a new path and a new behavior pattern by substituting a new habit for the old one, according to Tara Swart, senior lecturer at MIT, in her book *Neuroscience for Leadership*. "New connections and pathways are fragile, and only through repetition and practice can those connections be established enough to become habitual or default behaviors."

What can you put in place to reduce or replace procrastination as your "go to" response?

When people procrastinate, it's typically a task, action or project that they are avoiding. Whichever your reason, begin by breaking it down into more manageable chunks and then schedule time to tackle each chunk. If it feels too overwhelming to break up the whole project (and you're tempted to procrastinate), identify only the next three steps and schedule those actions. Still too big? Identify and schedule the next step. By scheduling, I mean use your preferred method to book appointments, whether it's a paper planner, phone, Outlook, calendar app or other means. The idea is to schedule a new habit and begin to use that new approach instead of the old one.

Ask yourself these questions:

- How can I start replacing a long-term habit that's been getting in my way? How would I like to be able to respond instead? (What's

1 www.fastcompany.com/3045424/what-it-takes-to-change-your-brains-patterns-after-age-25

the work-around?)

- What's the feeling or payoff I get when I use my default habit? What's a healthier way that I can get that same outcome?
- Where can I begin to make inroads to reducing the negative impacts of that habit on me? (Pick the low-hanging fruit if that's what you need to do to get yourself in motion.)
- How can I break my approach down into manageable, tangible pieces? (Start small, make progress and gain momentum.)

If you're stuck in this process and need help getting traction, get help from a trusted friend, mentor or coach.

Bring some levity to this approach. Be light about it. Treat it like play instead of work. Make it a fun experiment in discovering a new way to proceed.

Have a Backup Plan – What's Your Plan B?

Goal-setting for change typically starts with envisioning the ideal you're ultimately shooting for, as in the Wellness Vision you finalized in Chapter 10, followed by the ninety-day, thirty-day, and weekly goals.

Once you've set specific short-term goals, it's helpful to look at what actions are needed to achieve your goals, assess what's already on your plate (work, family and other commitments), what can be re-allocated, and block out the space for you to progress on your goals.

Now, it's time for you to start merrily on your way to take intentional action. You might find things are moving along well and then something happens. A relative gets sick and you need to spend time caregiving. Work changes occur that affect your work priorities, commitments and time. Your favorite Zumba instructor moves out of state. Some changes are harder and take longer to implement than you thought or require more planning and advance preparation than you anticipated.

The reality is, the universe won't always line up perfectly for you to seamlessly implement your goals. What's important to remember when life begins to take you off-course? Keep the big picture in mind (*why* you want to make these changes and the ultimate way of being you're aiming for) and follow a Plan B to keep yourself on track.

I've observed far too many cases of the all-or-nothing thinking that sabotages people. For example, one person's reaction to not being able to get to the gym four days this week because of their work schedule is to drop exercise altogether for the week. Another person, due to running late in the morning, grabs a muffin for breakfast on the way to work instead of having a vegetable omelet at home. Because they feel that small hiccup throws the whole day out the window, they proceed with going off-plan, eating anything they want the rest of the day.

You can start over in any moment (don't wait until the next day). Each second gives you an opportunity for a fresh start.

Again, you're creating *habits for a lifestyle*. Part of this journey is figuring out ways to dance with life. **Think of Plan B as the healthy actions you can take and ways that you can operate when times are tough or you feel squeezed.** For example, if you can't get to the gym as many days as you planned, consider these alternatives:

- Can you go at least one day?
- Can you walk, get creative about taking more steps during the day, or run around outside with your kids?
- Use a track at a local school.
- Have a walking meeting at work.
- Park further away from buildings, take the stairs instead of the elevator, use the restroom, water cooler or printer on a different floor in your building as a way to add flights of stairs, walk up and down the stairs in your home to your favorite playlist.
- Perform yard work, such as pulling weeds or raking leaves.
- Do exercises in front of the TV during commercials – try tricep dips off the couch, lunges, squats, sit-ups, push-ups and planks.

If you're facing eating challenges:

- Do your best to have healthy choices handy in your refrigerator and pantry, like fresh vegetables, fruits, nuts, healthy proteins, and "good" fats.

- If you go off track for a meal or snack, get back on track with the next meal.

- Have a tasty black decaf coffee or tea, or fruit-infused water after dinner instead of a nutrient-poor snack.

- If you know you will snack, choose fresh fruit or vegetables, lean proteins, and healthy fats as your top options.

- Pre-measure handfuls of nuts or cut-up vegetables for snacks, and have options like hummus, guacamole, and convenient proteins (like hard-boiled eggs) available.

Do your best to keep your commitment to your official goals and follow the initial plan that you set out. But when life gets in the way, don't throw the baby out with the bathwater. One small slip or not meeting your expectations doesn't mean it's all for nothing. Remember the big picture, your big whys and your work-arounds from when you first created your Wellness Vision. Review the plan you created in Chapter 10. Reread your list of strengths from Chapter 2 and your updated energizing story. If you can't hit all of a particular goal you're focused on this week, decide on an acceptable Plan B that moves you toward that goal. Which of your strengths can you bring to bear here? Use that fallback approach as needed to help yourself stay on track and get back to the original plan when you can.

Self-Sabotage Example One – Moving on from Distraction
Often what trips us up on the road to habit change and instilling new patterns that support us in our health isn't lack of information. We know what we want to do. But we're continuing to operate using the same routines (consciously or unaware) that keep us in our current state, including actions that distract us. Sorting/deleting email, paying bills, calling or texting a friend, getting absorbed in social media or news online. We can even include self-defeating behaviors like avoiding physical activity, staying up too late, jamming our schedules without allowing breathing room to regroup and restore ourselves, eating mindlessly as we zone out in front of the TV, watching movies, or otherwise letting ourselves be taken over by our phone, laptop or tablet.

Why do we self-sabotage? Partly because it's comfortable. It's a known entity. It may even feel good in the moment, or we gain a sense of tiny accomplishment from completing a minor task, even if it's not related to what matters in our health. While the outcomes don't help us move forward in burnout-proof living, we know what to expect. It's familiar territory.

Conversely, when we contemplate changing things, our brain rebels. It resists the change, in part, because we don't know what will happen as we start doing and/or being differently. It feels uncomfortable, and there's some level of uncertainty. We can even talk ourselves out of changing because we think it feels too hard. These dynamics tend to pull us toward busywork in another area where we rationalize that "at least we accomplished something." However, the reality is that we're letting opportunities to energize ourselves in burnout-proof ways slide away.

Consider how you distract yourself with busywork, when you postpone forward progress toward living your Wellness Vision. What if, when you felt that tug to do busywork, you instead stopped yourself and asked, "What am I resisting?" You could either ask yourself this out loud and have a conversation with yourself about it (seriously) or journal about it. I've personally used both methods multiple times to help me work through roadblocks in writing and editing *Ignition*'s manuscript.

When you are first planning to make such changes, realize you will waver more than once along the way. To prepare for these inevitable stumbles, create strategies from the very start for what you will do when things get uncomfortable and/or you begin falling back to the old habits you want to release.

- How will you dance with the discomfort?
- What will help you approach this as a growth opportunity instead of a reason to lose yourself in distraction?
- What boundaries are you ready to set, in order to fully commit with conviction to your elevated energy and burnout-proof life?

Self-Sabotage Example Two – Knowing vs. Doing
One of my favorite quotes, attributed to Goethe, is "Knowing is not enough; we must apply. Willing is not enough; we must do." I see this all the time, in conversations with my clients and also with women at various speaking

and networking events. I often have women tell me that they know all the things they need to do to improve their energy and feel better, even as they lament how hard it is to put such changes in place.

I agree that change can be difficult, and at times, feels uncomfortable. Know this going in and be prepared to work through and even grow through the discomfort. Take heed from this Randy Pausch quote: "The brick walls are there for a reason. The brick walls are not there to keep us out. The brick walls are there to give us a chance to show how badly we want something. Because the brick walls are there to stop the people who don't want it badly enough. They're there to stop the other people."

How badly do you want this energy and vitality in your life? Willpower is also a piece of it, and brain science plays a large role.

As previously mentioned by experts like Dr. Merzenich, Deborah Ancona, and Tara Swart, we have neural pathways in our brain that have been formed by the habits and rituals we've performed up until today. Those pathways will keep us maintaining the status quo until we take active steps to change. The good news, due to our brain's plasticity, is that you can create new habits and ultimately new paths in your brain, for the type of lifestyle you want to inhabit. The reality is that actively and consistently living these new habits takes time: an average of sixty-six days, according to a study[2] conducted by Phillippa Lally, a health psychology researcher at University College London, which was published in the *European Journal of Social Psychology*. I equate it to training a puppy to follow a new behavior: you repeat, repeat, repeat until the new behavior is instilled. It's a non-linear process, with forward progress and sliding backward, and plenty of ups and downs. It's the same way with us as humans: we're training our brains to behave in a new way.

To complicate matters, there's that thing called life. Yes, life happens: the challenge is figuring out how to dance with it and stay focused on what's most important to you, while keeping the fires of your health and wellness lit.

Trying to figure out every single step necessary for change can be overwhelming and keep us frozen in place. The trick is figuring out the next step – and then taking that one step. Then figuring out the next step, and so on. Self-reflection and journaling, talking to a trusted friend or working with an experienced coach can help you uncover your next step and put it into action.

2 www.onlinelibrary.wiley.com/doi/abs/10.1002/ejsp.674

There is no reason to wait. In fact, Alan Cohen sums this up beautiful-ly: "Do not wait until the conditions are perfect to begin. Beginning makes the conditions perfect." **Start where you are now**. Don't let your thinking talk yourself out of it. Act into the next step instead.

Perfectionism: When Being Perfect is Your Enemy

Think about it: when is it critical for things to be perfect in life? Surgical procedures are likely at or near the top of the list. Building the proper foun-dation and structure for a new home? Sure. That report you need done for a client? Having your home be immaculate and spotless? Always staying on top of the laundry? Being able to do it all, per society's standards? Presenting a Martha Stewart-esque "tablescape" for guests? Hmm ... maybe "perfect" isn't critically important by comparison.

At its worst, perfectionism can be downright exhausting, for both you and those with whom you interact. On the flip side, you can take pride and gratification in completing something in line with standards that you have established.

When I look at perfectionism through my health coaching lens, my concern is when perfectionist tendencies inhibit overall health and well-be-ing. Here are some questions to ask yourself if you'd like to assess whether perfectionism is an issue for you:

- [ ] Do you feel like you're twisting yourself in a pretzel more often than not to get everything done the way you want it done?
- [ ] Does your desire to have things just so and "perfect" constrain your ability to engage with the people and activities most important to you?
- [ ] What's behind your desire to have a certain thing perfect? Is it neces-sity, safety, or life or death (as in the surgery example)?
- [ ] Does it bring you joy or pleasure? Do you act this way out of a sense of duty or expectation?
- [ ] What's the story (or stories) you tell yourself about your need to have something perfect?
- [ ] How is being perfect in whatever situation serving you? How do you feel after completing something you consider perfect? (I know I've had to tell myself more than once that "the perfect is the enemy of the good.")

You might journal the answers to these questions or discuss them with a trusted friend. No judgment here: bring extreme compassion to this process. This is about creating awareness, so you can decide if and how you want to change your behavior.

After conducting this "perfection audit," consider what, if anything, you want to change.

Some places to begin:

- Identify areas in which you can **ease up on the perfection**. What is your new standard for "done" in each area?
- If you find yourself caught up in your perfection, **step back and take a big-picture view**. Ask yourself how much this will matter five or ten years from now? When you're on your deathbed and reviewing your life, will this be significant in the big scheme of things?
- **Take yourself through an inquiry** if you feel stuck in the thoughts you're having in a particular area, and feel pulled to make a change. Byron Katie's The Work[3] is a simple yet powerful four-question process for doing so.
- **Experiment initially with making small changes.** What can you unload? Where can you pare back but yet still be happy with the result? Must you attend every single event for which you receive an invite? Review your contact list for pruning, and play with options for designing your life around your health, to keep it sane, calm, and enjoyable. (Yes, I said *play* – be light with this!) Maybe it's time to retire former routines and create some new traditions?
- **Be like clay.** Be willing to mold and shape yourself in different ways. Refer back to this chapter and the Burnout-Proofing Dashboard as often as needed when you anticipate or encounter potential obstacles.
- **Implement change step by step, one at a time.** Attempting to take on new behaviors in multiple areas at once can be self-defeating. Instead, set yourself up for success. Choose one or two priority areas for improvement and focus on these first. Master those areas and then tackle the next.

3 www.thework.com

There is No Need to Go it Alone: Capitalize on Presence and Optimism, and Celebrate Progress

1. **If you are spiritual by nature, leverage that Source in attaining your energy and vitality goals.** Relying on and regularly connecting with this Source is a powerful ally. For those who believe in such a Source, it's a reassurance and strength that you always have available.

2. **Partner with a trusted physician.** Inform your primary care physician about the changes you want to make and why. They may have additional suggestions, resources and testing to recommend in support of your goals. If any form of exercise may put your health at risk, find out what you can safely do and what you should avoid. Finally, if you don't have a good working relationship with your primary care provider, fix the relationship or shop around for a new one.

3. **Establish a support system.** Have at least one person in your corner to support and assist you with implementing your changes. Possibilities include a health coach, a group (see Chapter 12 for more details), a best friend, a spouse, a workout buddy, your family or a roommate. Chapter 9 also has more details on creating your "A" team.

4. **Prioritize using your strengths for further development.** You'll move further faster (and feel better more quickly) when you first apply your past successes and strengths toward achieving your new patterns.

5. **Focus on the present instead of dwelling on the past.** What's in the past has passed by. The body, mindset or energy level you had then, what you did and didn't do – it's all in the rearview mirror. While your past brought you to today, it has zero *influence* (unless you allow it to) on the actions you take now, in this moment, to create your future. Your power is in the present moment. Choose the future you want and inject a bright new energy now to make it happen.

6. **Maintain an outlook of optimism.** Bringing negative judgment to something you haven't even started is like applying the brake when you're trying to accelerate. It delays forward movement (and makes you crabby in the process). As the Nike ad campaign says, just do it! Remember all the positive reasons why you want your wellness, and find ways to inject delight into the process. Choose fun forms of presence and compassion, try interesting new recipes, host or coordinate an energizing healthy social gathering, and pick inspiring rewards. Words have power. We've addressed that idea from multiple angles throughout this book. Live into a more uplifting story. Talk yourself higher. Treat yourself like the blessing you are. Change the "shoulds" into "coulds."

7. **Celebrate milestones in healthy ways.** Again, it's all about the journey. Did you write in your food/exercise journal every day this week? Did you test out a new boundary-setting technique? Great! Treat yourself to a magazine, a new song download, or other small trinket that brings you a few moments of happiness (instead of eating a candy bar). Call a friend you haven't spoken to in a while. Do a happy dance! Establish bigger rewards for when you hit the more substantive goals.

~~~~~~~~~~~~~~~~~~~~~

Before we close out this guidance for your energizing adventure, turn to Chapter 12 for some final parting words and ways you can be part of a larger community of professional women living in burnout-proof ways.

CHAPTER TWELVE

Celebrate Your Success and Join an Ignited Movement

"Instead of rushing, simply be sure to step forward in every way you can with certainty and grace."

~ JEN ERAMITH

ou did it! Celebrate what you've accomplished thus far in moving through *Ignition*. Give yourself the space to affirm what you've learned and what's changed or different for you after travelling through this book. Step back and ponder this achievement. Say it out loud, share your discoveries with a friend, and document your new patterns.

While I commend you on all the note-taking, experimentation, discovery and planning up to this point, I implore you to keep going. Maintain your forward momentum, giving your best each day, each moment. Acknowledge each triumph as you instill the changes, step by step, that you've chosen. The world is waiting for you to ignite!

If you still find yourself waiting to make changes for increased energy and burnout-proof living, think about it: what are you postponing? Are you waiting for things to be a certain way? Is the devil you know more comfortable than the one you don't?

These days, many people are held hostage by fear, worry and/or uncertainty. Numerous old rules for how to operate no longer apply. In our "busyness" with all our responsibilities, we can sometimes fall into the trap of losing sight of the big picture and forgetting what's most important to us, or our deep desires. Further, such "busy-ness" can keep us from seeing alternatives or creative approaches.

I'm convinced our current times are teaching us all to find ways to work better with uncertainty. A tip: the way to *not* work better is to remain stuck in the fear of the unknown of moving forward. When you hear the voice of fear or concern about the unknown, let that be your trigger to consciously choose another perspective about whatever is scaring or concerning you.

Reframe FEAR to mean Face Everything And Rise (an acronym a client shared with me), and use the following steps:

- Press pause and re-center yourself.
- Re-read your energizing story, Wellness Vision and big whys.
- Think of the ripple effects that you will generate through your energized, burnout-proof living.
- Look at the work-arounds you identified in Chapter 3.
- Ask yourself, "What's possible?"

Repeat as needed, especially when you feel surrounded by the crazy busy whirlwind of others around you, or feel yourself losing steam, drifting toward chronic doing and neglecting being. Use the above steps to bring order to your universe and restore harmony.

You've come far. You've played in the sandbox. You've dedicated time, energy and space to yourself. You've had some aha moments that you've parlayed into a plan. You've had a taste of what you and those whom you touch gain by purposefully igniting your energy. You've committed.

You've removed the barriers in the way of your resilience and vitality. You've deemed what earns the right to be on your plate now, and what deserves your energy and attention. Keep giving yourself the breathing room and fuel that lets you thrive. You are in charge of how you experience, respond to, and contribute to life. Use *Ignition* as your sanctuary, a place you can always return to, for maintaining your energized, burnout-proof living, and to regroup when you need reminders. Don't limit yourself to taking the journey through *Ignition* just once and consider it "one and done." You can come back any time you need a tune-up or an energetic lift.

As we move through different phases of life, we may have new responsibilities and situations that present additional challenges in keeping ourselves energized and burnout-proof. After we fully establish a particular Wellness Vision in our lives, there might be a future time where we need a new and different Wellness Vision. Further, each essential element of the

Burnout-Proofing Dashboard has its own inherent layers, and we might go deeper into some elements in later life phases.

For now, I'll offer you one final exercise. Write a letter to yourself, telling you what you most want to remember, from your experience in moving through *Ignition*. Put that letter in a self-addressed stamped envelope, and seal it. Give it to a trusted family member or friend, and ask them to mail it to you three months from now.

As you move forward and make progress, I encourage you to also get others on board and connect with more women who've retired the old ways of depleting themselves and have embraced these ways of being present, fueling, relating, leading the compassion dance with heart, and creating space and inner balance. Be part of a community of role models actively putting these principles into place, to share your success stories, brainstorm and collaborate on navigating challenges, and keep on track in firing up your energy.

Let's create a global ripple effect of ever-increasing groups of women who view self-care as sacred instead of selfish, by performing in the following ways:

- Walking the talk of inner balance and the rhythm of doing and being before work-life balance.
- Modeling being engaged while energized instead of crazy busy and depleted, as a badge of honor.
- Contributing in ways that exhilarate versus exhaust us.
- Approaching our challenges with more ease instead of more pushing.
- Deliberately prioritizing instead of attempting to do it all.
- Being open to receiving help from human, intuitive and/or spiritual resources.

Here are some suggestions for how you can build or join a community:

- Share this book. Spread the word and/or gift copies of *Ignition*! If you work in a company or other organization, share it with your female colleagues. If you manage other women, share it with your staff. If you are in an association or networking group, share it with your female members. If you work in a hospital or healthcare setting, share it with your female coworkers and patients. Share it with your doctor and other healthcare professionals. Share it with the women important to you in your various walks of life, from family members and friends to coworkers and clients.

- Host your book group or a "ladies' night in" with friends, neighbors, coworkers or family members where you share this book, your impressions, and how it impacted you. Invite these women to join an "Ignition Circle" to meet regularly, whether in person, via conference call, or online, to move through the book (perhaps one chapter or one part per meeting) and discuss their reactions, outcomes of experiments, and what they're choosing to implement in their lives.

- Join the Women Igniting Energized Burnout-Proof Living Facebook Group[1] and start contributing your stories.

- Create a supportive corporate culture. If you work in a corporate setting and have influence on the company culture, reflect on how well your company's environment supports energized, burnout-proof living for your employees. Are breaks encouraged? Is eating lunch away from a desk modeled from the top? Are there opportunities to move and recharge? Do email and messaging expectations allow employees to truly disconnect from work communication during off-hours daily (and on days off)? Do employees feel safe to request help or guidance to reset work priorities when they feel overloaded? What cultural shifts are needed to support the well-being of your employees?

Like Dorothy in *The Wizard of Oz*, you've had the magic of the ruby slippers all along. I simply gave you the awareness, in this book, to guide you through the twists and turns of your unique yellow brick road that leads toward your new harmonized home of energized, burnout-proof living. Remember that there are multiple ways of doing and being. You are in the driver's seat in terms of the outlook you hold, the expectations you set, the words you use, and the actions you take. Your core power stems from inner balance. When in doubt, return there first.

---

1 www.facebook.com/groups/IgnitionGroup

I wrote this prayer below and continually reflected upon its words as I created *Ignition*. I share it with you in the hopes that it will provide some initial inspiration in igniting your energetic essence and letting it shine through.

> *Help me continually deepen my inner stillness.*
> *Remind me to see the true essence of others and come*
> *from my essence in how I serve and connect.*
> *Escort me into being the loving consciousness I am*
> *in as many moments as possible.*
> *Remind me to play and stay light with a variety of*
> *energies and the wonder that is.*
> *Maintaining presence in the now,*
> *I am grateful for the awareness of consciousness*
> *flowing through me.*
> *I get out of the way and allow.*

Shine and glow on! Or, in the words of St. Ignatius Loyola:

> *"Go forth and set the world on fire!"*

About the Author

Chris Vasiliadis inspires people to use their well-being as their secret weapon for successfully leading their work and non-work life. Since founding her business, Priority Wellness, in 2008, she has helped countless individuals energize their health and improve their performance. Blending compassion, firmness, and fun, she works with those who are tired of putting their health on the back burner, unhappy/unfocused in their wellness, and/or concerned about burnout. As a National Board Certified Health & Wellness Coach, she works one-on-one and in group settings in a variety of ways, including with private clients, a corporation's employees, or patients in a healthcare environment.

She speaks on various related wellness topics at networking groups and events, conferences, inside companies and higher education settings. Chris has been interviewed on different podcasts, and is available for future interviews.

Chris's clients ultimately instill habits that make their health thrive, burnout-proof their lives, and powerfully perform at their best. Choosing to prioritize her wellness after her multiple sclerosis diagnosis in 2005, Chris has been relapse-free since 2007. She's a voracious reader with an affinity for historical fiction, a huge foodie who loves day trips and visiting different restaurants, and a die-hard Red Sox fan. Chris lives outside the Boston area with her husband, Peter.

For media inquiries, visit www.prioritywellness.com/media.

Acknowledgments

"None of us, including me, ever do great things. But we can all do small things, with great love, and together we can do something wonderful."

– MOTHER TERESA

I certainly was not alone in creating *Ignition* and have many people to thank.

Kate Victory Hannisian, whose main role was my editor. You wore multiple hats in helping me flesh out various content and structural changes, were a powerful and patient sounding board the many times I felt stuck in the muck, and an incredible resource for all things self-publishing. I cannot imagine what this book would have looked like without your insights and word mastery, from the initial book proposal all the way through the finalized manuscript. My deepest thanks to you!

Lisa McKenna, my book designer. You "got" *Ignition* from day one, and brought it to life with a cover and layout beyond what I could have envisioned. Your visual and branding gifts are a treasure!

My beta reviewers. I deeply appreciate the time you spent in your reviews and providing thoughtful feedback. Thank you for helping me to further shape *Ignition* to optimally connect with future readers. A special shout-out to Deb: my bestie for over thirty-five years and counting – love ya, darlin'!

Every person I interviewed and who shared a story that I included in this book. I know your stories will speak to and help many other women.

All my clients, speaking attendees, and anyone with whom I've had a conversation about burnout and/or their pace of life. You help me keep on top of the pulse of what's real for you in maintaining a healthy lifestyle, and it's my consistent privilege to serve you in whatever ways I can.

The fellow members of my women's business roundtable: Judy, Jane, Kate and Jennifer. Thank you for your friendship, encouragement, and brainstorming, especially in creating the Burnout-Proofing Dashboard figure.

Other self-published authors. Your accomplishments and generous advice helped me stay the course the many times I stalled in the over two years of writing *Ignition*.

Hay House and their Writer's Workshop. Attending the Hay House 2016 Writer's Workshop in Chicago started me on the path to writing the book proposal for *Ignition*. My proposal submission to their publishing contest didn't win, but it forced me to write the first two chapters, and begin my self-publishing journey. I'm not sure when I would have begun writing *Ignition*, had I not attended that conference. Thank you, Amanda, for "igniting" me to attend that conference and sharing that experience with me!

Every. Single. Person. who asked in the over two years I spent writing *Ignition*, "How's the book coming?" Your interest and cheering me on were a huge part of what inspired me to continue stepping forward.

Mom. Thank you for attending one of my early presentations on the Burnout-Proofing Dashboard and for being such a courageous example of self-compassion and strong energy, especially in the years since Dad's passing. I am often in awe of you, and I love you always.

Peter. There were numerous times I could have dropped this project. Your unending love and support were instrumental in enabling me to persist and follow this bucket list dream through to completion. As I often say, it's like I won the lottery when I met you and later became your partner for life. "I love you" doesn't seem to fully capture my emotions.

References and Resources

BOOKS

A New Earth: Awakening to Your Life's Purpose
by Eckhart Tolle. Plume. 2005.

Loving What Is: Four Questions That Can Change Your Life
by Byron Katie. Three Rivers Press. 2002.

Essentialism: The Disciplined Pursuit of Less
by Greg McKeown. Crown Business. 2014.

The Artist's Way: A Spiritual Path to Higher Creativity
by Julia Cameron. Tarcher/Putnam. 1992.

The Myth of Multitasking: How "Doing It All" Gets Nothing Done
by Dave Crenshaw. Jossey-Bass. 2008.

*The Power of Full Engagement: Managing Energy, Not Time, Is the Key to
High Performance and Personal Renewal*
by Jim Loehr and Tony Schwartz. The Free Press. 2003.

Being Peace
by Thich Nhat Hanh. Parallax Press. 2005.

The Confidential Clerk
by T.S. Eliot. Harcourt Brace. 1954.

Life is Good: The Book. How to Live with Purpose & Enjoy the Ride
by Bert and John Jacbos. National Geographic. 2015.

Soft-Wired: How the New Science of Brain Plasticity Can Change Your Life
by Dr. Michael Merzenich. Parnassus Publishing. 2013.

*Neuroscience for Leadership: Harnessing the Brain Gain Advantage
(The Neuroscience of Business)*
by Tara Swart, Kitty Chisholm, and Paul Brown. Palgrave Macmillan. 2015.

WEBSITES

Meetup: www.meetup.com

The Work: www.thework.com

VIA Character Strengths Assessment: www.viacharacter.org

Mark Silver Heart of Business Course: www.heartofbusiness.com

Ergotron: www.juststand.org

TripAdvisor: www.tripadvisor.com

Groupon: www.groupon.com

LivingSocial: www.livingsocial.com

VIDEO

Louie Schwartzberg: Nature. Beauty. Gratitude.

www.ted.com/talks/louie_schwartzberg_nature_beauty_gratitude

Notes

Notes

Ignition

Notes

Made in the USA
Middletown, DE
15 May 2019